"You had a baby, didn't you?"

The blood drained from Imogen's face. "How did you find out?" she croaked.

"By accident."

"I'm sorry." She sounded as feeble-minded as she felt.

"Sorry for what?" Joe blazed. "For the way I found out I'd fathered a child, or that I found out at all? You could have told me yourself, at the time. But let me guess why you didn't. Donnelly genes didn't measure up to what it took to be a Palmer heir. It was easier to erase the mistake before anyone found out about it. How am I doing so far, princess? Batting a hundred?"

"You couldn't be more wrong," Imogen whispered.

"Then what the hell happened to my child?"

Catherine Spencer, once an English teacher, fell into writing through eavesdropping on a conversation about Harlequin romances. Within two months she changed careers and sold her first book to Mills & Boon® in 1984. She moved to Canada from England thirty years ago and lives in Vancouver. She is married to a Canadian and has four grown children—two daughters and two sons—plus three dogs and a cat. In her spare time she plays the piano, collects antiques, and grows tropical shrubs.

Recent titles by the same author:

A NANNY IN THE FAMILY
DANTE'S TWINS

THE SECRET DAUGHTER

BY
CATHERINE SPENCER

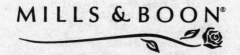

MILLS & BOON®

All the characters in this book have no existence outside the imagination of the author, and have no relation whatsoever to anyone bearing the same name or names. They are not even distantly inspired by any individual known or unknown to the author, and all the incidents are pure invention.

First published in Great Britain 1998
Harlequin Mills & Boon Limited,
Eton House, 18-24 Paradise Road, Richmond, Surrey TW9 1SR

© Kathy Garner 1998

ISBN 0 263 81438 6

Set in Times Roman 10½ on 12 pt.
01-9901-51622 C1

Printed and bound in Norway
by AIT Trondheim AS, Trondheim

CHAPTER ONE

TANYA seized the crumpled invitation from the waste-basket where Imogen had tossed it, smoothed out the creases and said, "What do you mean, you're going to send your regrets? Your high school principal's retiring and your hometown's celebrating its centennial anniversary. This is a heaven-sent opportunity, Imogen!"

"To do what?" Imogen barely lifted her head from the design she was working on for Mrs. Lynch-Carter's windows.

"Why, to mend fences with your mother, of course. Or do you plan to wait until she's dead before you attempt a reconciliation? Because if you do, my dear, let me assure you that you'll be eaten up with guilt for the rest of your life."

"If my mother wants to see me, Tanya, she knows where I live."

"But you're the one who refused to go home again. It strikes me it's up to you to be the one to make the first move now." Tanya adopted her most winning tone, the one she used on clients who mistakenly believed that money and good taste automatically went hand in hand. "Let's face it, Imogen. You've been dreadfully hurt by the estrangement, and the odds are your mother has, too."

"I doubt it," Imogen replied, recalling the speed with which Suzanne Palmer had hustled her out of town and out of the country within days of learning

5

of her daughter's fall from grace. "When I needed her the most, my mother abandoned me."

"Does it make you feel better to go on punishing her for it?" Tanya persisted. "Do you never wonder if perhaps she regrets the way she acted but doesn't quite know how to go about rectifying her mistake? We're a long time dead, kiddo, and it's too late then to put things right. Do it now, while you still can, is my advice."

If truth be known, Imogen had thought the same thing herself many times. And lately, she'd missed her mother more than usual. Having someone care enough to want to orchestrate every facet of her life was better than having no one at all.

Was it possible they could start over, not as parent and child but as two adults with close ties and a mutual respect for each other? The teenager in trouble with nowhere to turn had evolved into an independent twenty-seven-year-old thoroughly in charge of her own life. That being so, should she put aside her injured pride and offer the olive branch?

Never one to lose an argument if she could possibly avoid it, Tanya said, "She's a widow, and you're her only child, for pity's sake! Who else has she got in her old age?"

The mere idea of Suzanne growing old struck Imogen as ludicrous. Her mother simply wouldn't allow it. She'd be tucked, lifted and dyed to within an inch of her life before she'd submit to the wear and tear of time. Still, she was almost sixty. And it had been nine years.

Sensing she was winning this particular debate, Tanya pressed her advantage. "If it's an excuse you're looking for that will allow you to save face, you've got it here,'' she said, tapping the invitation. ''What better reason for simply showing up at the door and saying something cool and offhand along the lines of, 'I just happened to be in the neighborhood and thought I'd stop by to see how you're doing'?''

''Whatever else her faults, my mother is no fool, Tanya. She'd see through that in a flash.''

''And maybe it wouldn't matter if she did. Sometimes a little white lie is the kindest route to take, especially if it spares people having their noses rubbed in past mistakes.''

Put like that, it seemed mean-spirited and just plain immature not to seize the opportunity to end the estrangement. And Imogen liked to think that, in the years since Joe Donnelly had sped in and out of her life with the brief impact of a meteor shooting through space, she'd grown up enough to deal with whatever had to be dealt with and not fall apart in the process.

Still, there was more involved in going back to Rosemont than dealing with her mother. There was—

''Of course, if there's some other reason holding you back, some other person you're afraid to face, perhaps…''

The knowing, secret little smile with which Tanya finished the sentence found its mark. Too quickly and much too defensively, Imogen retorted, ''Like who?''

''Oh, the name Joe Donnelly comes to mind for some reason.''

Cursing herself for falling into so obvious a trap, Imogen said blandly, ''I can't imagine why. I haven't given him a thought in years.''

Tanya was tall and elegantly thin, beautiful and enviably sophisticated, cultured, educated and gifted.

But none of that stopped her from crowing with the delight of a child, ''Liar, liar, pants on fire!''

The devil of it was, she was right. If Imogen were to be honest, she'd have to admit she'd never been able to forget Joe Donnelly. Not that she didn't try—and even come close to succeeding much of the time. Weeks, even months might go by without her thinking of him, especially when she was involved in a project. Helping a client decide between faux marble or French silk wall treatments didn't exactly trigger her memory of him.

But when it came to romance, she'd find herself comparing the current man in her life to a black-haired, sultry-eyed rebel with a smile as handsome and dangerously knowing as sin and a way with words that could persuade a saint to stray.

By the time she'd tell herself that, in the nine years since she'd seen him, Joe Donnelly probably had de-generated into a shiftless, beer-swigging layabout, run to fat and, like his father, lost most of his hair, it was too late. Whatever spark might have existed between her and the Tom, Dick or Harry of the moment had already fizzled and died.

''I gather from your silence that I've touched a nerve,'' Tanya observed.

''Not at all.''

''Oh, come on, Imogen! You're still hung up on the guy. Admit it.''

''I remember him, of course,'' Imogen said, truly trying to be objective, ''but to say I'm hung up on him is absurd. The last time I saw him, I'd just turned eighteen and was barely out of school—a girl with a crush on a man who seemed attractive because he was a few years older and had something of a reputation around town. I've matured since then. Motorcycle hoods no longer strike me as appealing.''

''A woman never loses her fascination for the man who introduces her to love.''

''I have.''

''Then there's no reason you can't go home again, is there?''

''No reason at all,'' Imogen said, the same pride that had kept her from reconciling with her mother rising up to back her into another kind of corner.

''And since you're so mature, you'll find it in your heart to kiss and make up with Mother?''

Well, why not? Imogen chewed the end of her pencil and considered the merits of such a move. Going home would necessarily mean raking up some painful aspects of the past, but wasn't it time she laid to rest the ghosts that had haunted her for over eight years? The important thing was to be selective in her remembering, to focus only on her relationship with her mother and not to allow herself to become bogged down in useless regrets over a man who had never spared her a second thought once he'd introduced her to sex.

As long as she stuck to that resolve and remained in charge of her emotions, nothing could really go wrong. Or so she thought.

''All right, you've convinced me,'' she told Tanya. ''I'll accept the invitation and see if I can't work something out with my mother.''

But nothing went as planned, starting with her arrival, one afternoon toward the end of June, at Deepdene Grange, her family's estate and possibly the only property in town whose house warranted the description "mansion."

"Madam is not at home," the maid, a total stranger, informed her, standing guard at the door as if she feared Imogen might take the place by storm.

Imogen stared at her, speechless. In the month before she'd set out from Vancouver, she'd suffered more than a few qualms about the wisdom of her decision to go home again, but her misgivings had taken serious hold when she'd picked up her rental car at Pearson International and headed northeast, away from the sticky humidity of Toronto and toward cottage country. What if all she did was make things worse and widen the gulf between her and her mother?

By the time she'd reached Clifton Hill, Rosemont's toniest residential area, and turned in at Deepdene's big iron gates, nervous anticipation the size and texture of a lump of clay hung in the pit of her stomach. But she'd come this far, and nothing, she thought, could deter her.

Except this.

"Not at home?" she echoed, shaking her head in the way people do when they're not sure they understand the language being spoken.

The maid didn't so much as blink. "I'm afraid not."

But it was four o'clock on Saturday, the hour when, winter or summer for as far back as Imogen could remember, Suzanne Palmer had taken afternoon tea in the solarium prior to dressing for whatever social function she was holding or attending that evening.

As though to verify that she'd come to the right house, Imogen peered over the maid's shoulder. The foyer looked exactly as it always had. The Waterford crystal chandelier sparkled in the sunlight, the carved oak banister gleamed, the hand-knotted Persian stair runner glowed softly. Even the bowl of roses on the console beneath the ornate gilt mirror might have been the very same as that occupying the identical spot, the day she'd walked out of her home almost nine years before, believing, at the time, that she would never return.

The maid shifted to block her view and narrowed the angle of the open door. "Who may I say called?"

"What?" Already becoming enmeshed in the past, Imogen gave herself a mental shake and steered her attention to the present. "Oh! Her daughter."

Too well-trained to betray surprise by more than a faint lifting of her eyebrows, the maid said, "Madam is gone for the weekend but she should be home by late tomorrow afternoon. She didn't mention anything about a guest."

Unwilling to give her mother the chance to reject her a second time, Imogen had booked a room at the town's only good hotel—a wise precaution indeed, since Suzanne Palmer clearly had declined to inform her current household staff that she had a daughter. "She wasn't expecting me. I'm staying at the Briarwood. However, I would like to leave a note telling her I'm in town."

"I'll be happy to give her a message."

"I'd prefer to leave a note." Not giving her time to protest, Imogen stepped past the maid into the foyer.

She'd have thought her familiarity with the layout of Deepdene Grange and the exact location of her mother's private sitting room would have lent credibility to her claim of having grown up in the house but, face tight with suspicion, the maid stuck to her like glue.

"Madam prefers not to have her private papers disturbed," she objected, as Imogen sat at Suzanne's pretty little Empire writing desk and lowered the lid.

"Madam" had preferred not to acknowledge her wayward daughter's behavior nine years ago, but she hadn't been able to change its outcome. "I'll make sure you're not held responsible for my actions," Imogen said, "and if it eases your mind any, I have no intention at all of invading my mother's privacy."

In fact, though, she did just that. Reaching into one of the pigeonholes for a slip of paper, she accidentally dislodged a sheaf of canceled checks, some of which fluttered into her lap and others to the polished floor.

With an exclamation of distress, the maid stooped to retrieve those on the floor while Imogen gathered the rest. "No harm done," she said, aligning hers into a neat pile by tapping the edges smartly on the desk.

"But they were arranged by number," the young maid almost whimpered. "Madam is *very* particular about things like that."

Then little had changed, after all! "She always was," Imogen said, "but as long as they're left the way I found them, she'll never know the difference."

Quickly, she shuffled the various checks into the proper sequence: number 489, made out to the Municipality of Rosemont for annual property taxes, number 488 to the telephone company and number 487, a tidy sum payable to St. Martha's, her mother's old private school, in Norbury, about forty miles west of Niagara Falls.

Imogen wasn't unduly curious or surprised. Suzanne had always contributed generously to those causes she deemed worthy and prided herself on her largess. It was only where her daughter and certain segments of

Rosemont society were concerned that she lacked charity.

With the checks restored to order and replaced in the desk, it took Imogen only a moment to write her note. "I'm not planning to stay in the area more than a few days," she said, handing the folded slip of paper to the maid, "so I'd appreciate it if you'd make sure my mother receives this as soon as she comes home."

She was barely out the door before the maid closed it behind her. Faced with empty hours to fill, Imogen drove slowly toward the center of town, searching out familiar landmarks and, despite her best intentions, remembering too much.

Banners proclaiming the town's centennial anniversary flanked the columns fronting the courthouse, baskets of flowering plants hung from the wrought-iron lampposts on Main Street, Judge Merriweather's house had been turned into an accountant's office, and the old Rosemont Medical Building was now a youth center.

Once past the railroad station, Main Street split in two, the right lane following the curve of the lakeshore and the left leading to Lister's Meadows, where the Donnellys used to live.

"Definitely the wrong side of the tracks," her mother had determined when, the summer she turned fifteen, Imogen had insisted on attending a birthday party there. But Imogen had loved the friendly neighborliness of the area. Although the houses were small and close together, with long narrow gardens at the back, there were no fences separating one place from the next, no signs warning trespassers to stay away.

The Donnelly house had been at the end of the last

street, she recalled, with a creek running beside it. But whether or not they'd moved, she had no idea. She and Patsy Donnelly had lost touch when Imogen went to stay with her mother's cousin the autumn after her eighteenth birthday and Joe…

Oh, Joe Donnelly had not cared enough to pursue a relationship with Imogen Palmer and had left Ontario within days of his one-night stand with the richest girl in town. He did not deserve to be remembered.

So there was no earthly reason for her to head east to where Donnelly's Garage used to be open for business fifteen hours a day, seven days a week. Did she seriously expect to see Sean Donnelly manning the pumps or Mr. Donnelly bent over the open hood of a car? Or Joe Donnelly straddling his idling Harley-Davidson and surveying the unending parade of girls willing to show off their physical assets in the hope of luring him even further into temptation than his natural inclination had already led him?

Apparently she did. How else to account for the wave of disappointment that washed over her when she saw that what used to be Donnelly's Garage was now a slick, twelve-pump, self-serve gas station owned by a major oil company? She ought to have rejoiced that nothing remained to remind her.

"Oh, grow up, Imogen!" she muttered, annoyed by what could only be described as blatant self-indulgence. "Instead of wasting time dwelling on a man who, except for one memorable occasion, never spared you a second glance, think about what you're going to say when you see your mother again because, whatever else might happen, at least *she* can't deny you ever existed!"

Swinging the car in an illegal U-turn and consigning

Joe Donnelly to that part of her past she had determined not to revisit, she headed to her hotel. It was
almost six o'clock. By the time she'd showered and
changed, it would be dinnertime.

Imogen's room on the second floor of the Briarwood
was handsomely furnished and looked out on the lake.
Preferring the flower-scented breeze to the sterile dis-
comfort of the air conditioner, she opened the French
windows and stepped out on the small balcony over-
hanging the gardens. Immediately below, a wedding
reception was in progress, with tables set out on the
lawn and a wasp-waisted bride, lovely in white or-
ganza and orange blossom, holding court beneath an
arbor of roses.

Imogen was unprepared for the envy that stabbed
through her at the sight of that young woman. Not
because she had a husband and Imogen had not—re-
maining single was, after all, her choice—but because
the bride wore an air of innocence Imogen had lost
when she was a teenager.

Though only just twenty-seven, she felt suddenly
old. And bitter. By most standards, she had all those
things that mattered in today's world. She was successful, she had money, and men seemed to find her
attractive enough that they asked her out often. One
or two had even proposed marriage.

But inside, where it counted, she was empty. Had
been empty for the better part of nine years. And it
would take a lot more than a shower and a good dinner
to restore her to the kind of optimism that left the bride
so luminous with joy.

If only...

No! Grief softened with time, the sharp edge of

heartbreak melted into kindly nostalgia, and only a fool dwelled on horror. She might have been born and raised in Rosemont, but her future lay half a continent away in Vancouver, and she'd do well to keep reminding herself of that.

The courthouse clock struck seven. Too keyed up to face dinner, Imogen changed out of the smart linen suit she'd worn for the meeting with her mother and slipped into a thin cotton dress and sandals. A brisk walk would go a lot further toward relaxing her and insuring a good night's rest than beef Wellington or lobster thermidor in the formal elegance of the hotel dining room.

Although the air was warm, a slight breeze blew across the lake, stirring the surface of the water to dazzling ripples. Slipping on a pair of sunglasses, Imogen turned right at the foot of the hotel steps and headed west on the shoreline boardwalk, past the pier, the public beach and the band shell, then through the park, to end up some forty minutes later at what used to be the Rosemont Tea Garden.

Like so many other places, though, this, too, had undergone change. A smart awning covered the fenced patio where faded sun umbrellas had once given shade to patrons. Wicker furniture and woven place mats had replaced the old plastic tables and chairs. And instead of scones, homemade strawberry jam and tea served in mismatched china cups, a chalkboard menu propped by the patio gate offered a selection of chilled soups, salads and trendy pasta dishes.

Tempted by the thought of langostino salad, Imogen passed through the gate and waited to be seated. It was as she was being shown to a table that a voice exclaimed, "Imogen Palmer, is that you hiding behind those dark glasses?"

Startled, she looked around to see Patsy Donnelly, of all people, rising from a table just inside the patio's wrought-iron railing, her dark blue eyes and black hair so much like her brother's that, without warning, all Imogen's fine resolutions to stay in charge of herself and the events surrounding her wilted like roses left too long without water.

Mistaking her stunned silence for nonrecognition, Patsy said, "It's me, Imogen. Patsy Donnelly. Surely you haven't forgotten?"

"Of course not," Imogen said weakly. "I'm just surprised to see you here, that's all."

But if her response was less than enthusiastic, Patsy didn't seem to notice. Inviting Imogen to join her by pulling out one of the chairs at her table, she laughed and said, "I don't see why. It is Rosemont's centennial celebration, after all, not to mention Miss Duncliffe's big retirement bash. Just about everyone we went to school with is in town, even Joe. I'm just the first of a long line of familiar faces you'll be running into. How long are you staying?"

"Not long at all," Imogen said, suppressing the urge to bolt to the hotel, pack her bags, race to the airport and climb aboard the first flight headed west. Why was Joe Donnelly here when, from everything she'd ever heard, the only time he'd shown the slightest interest in school had been during basketball season?

Patsy flagged down a waiter, asked him to bring an extra wineglass, then sat regarding Imogen expectantly. "So, tell me about yourself. Are you married? Do you have any children?"

"No." Her answer was brief to the point of rude, but not for the life of her could Imogen get past the fact that Joe Donnelly was in town. She couldn't face him. It was as simple as that! Bad enough that he was resurrecting himself in her memory without her having to confront him in the flesh.

Patsy leaned forward, her pretty, vivid face creased with concern. "Did I ask the wrong question, Imogen?"

Realizing she was committing the kind of social gaffe that would have put her mother under the table with shame, Imogen struggled to rally her composure. "No, no. I'm just…surprised you remember me."

It wasn't an entirely moronic observation. She'd been tutored by a governess until she was thirteen and would have been sent to boarding school after that if Suzanne had had her way. But Imogen, desperate to be "ordinary" like the teenagers she saw around town, had prevailed on her father to allow her to attend Rosemont High.

But she'd never really belonged. Her circle of friends had been limited to those few girls her mother had decided were sufficiently gently reared to associate with a Palmer. In fact, she could count on one hand the number who'd been allowed to set foot inside Deepdene's gates to enjoy a game of tennis or dabble their well-bred toes in the swimming pool.

Although Patsy had been universally popular with her schoolmates, she had not met Suzanne's rigid standards, and the best Imogen had been able to establish with her was an association that, though friendly, had rarely extended beyond the school grounds.

"Not remember you?" Patsy hooted, gesturing to the waiter to fill both glasses from the open wine bottle on the table. "Imogen, you were the most unforgettable girl ever to pass through the school doors. When we weren't all terrified of you, we wanted to be just like you. You were—" she stopped and waved both hands as if invoking divine intervention "—a princess in our midst. Mysterious, regal. The Grace Kelly of Rosemont High, which is why—"

"Why what?" Surprised by Patsy's sudden awkward silence, Imogen leaned forward, intrigued. "What were you going to say?"

Patsy shrugged and made a big production of wrapping her paper napkin around the base of her wineglass. "Oh, just that, well, I thought you might be...with someone."

"No one special, no."

"I see." Still noticeably ill at ease, Patsy continued to find her napkin fascinating. "So, um, where do you live and what do you do?"

Imogen continued to regard her curiously. The girl she'd known in school was never at a loss for words, yet Patsy was floundering. "I work for an interior design company in Vancouver."

"Interior design!" Her vivacity resurfacing, Patsy grinned delightedly. "My, that has a real Imogen ring to it!"

"Simply put, it means I help rich women decide what color they should paint their bathrooms."

"I suspect it involves a lot more than that. You always had a real eye for style. You're the only girl I ever knew who could make blue jeans and a T-shirt look like high fashion."

"Probably because the only way I could persuade my mother to let me wear them in the first place was if they had designer labels sewn on them. But what

about you, Patsy? Any husband or children in your
life?''

''No husband, but there are children. I'm an aunt
twice over. Dennis is seven and a half, and Jack will
be six in October. And they're adorable, as you'll see
for yourself.'' She raised her wineglass, said,
''Cheers! Lovely to see you again,'' then went on
without a pause. ''Joe took the boys fishing for min-
nows in Flanagan's Slough, and I met some of the old
gang from school for dinner here earlier, but I don't
have a car to get home, so he's stopping by to give
me a lift.''

Imogen sat there like stone, unable to drum up anything resembling a coherent response to the stream of
information Patsy directed her way. Whatever else
she'd thought herself prepared for, the possibility that
Joe had settled down to family life had never once
occurred to her. If she'd been struck by a bolt of light-
ning, the shock couldn't have been more acute. *But
that's not fair,* she wanted to howl. *If he was going to
fall in love anyway, why couldn't it have been with
me?*

''Did you go into nursing as you planned?'' she
managed to ask with a semblance of normality when
Patsy stopped speaking.

''Oh, yes. Got my degree, took some post-grad
training in neonatal care and have worked at Toronto
General on the maternity floor ever since, looking after
the premature babies. I love it, although it's heart-
breaking at times. But the miracle of birth never ceases
to thrill me, especially when a baby survives despite
the odds.''

The sun still sparkled on the lake, but Imogen was
lost in a sudden darkness. How was it possible for old

pain to rise up and consume a person so thoroughly
that her vision was clouded by it and a giant fist
seemed to be squeezing the life out of her heart? "I
have to go," she said, rising up from her chair almost
violently.

"But you only just got here!"

"I know. But I just remembered—"

Too much. Far, far too much!

In her haste, she stumbled against the table and sent
the contents of her handbag flying. Her wallet fell out
and hit the patio with such a thump that the change
purse opened, scattering loose coins under the adjoining table.

As if they'd been waiting for just such a windfall,
two small boys appeared out of the lengthening shadows and, like beggars foraging for scraps, scooped up
the shiny nickels and dimes with shrieks of glee.

Imogen didn't need the chill of premonition creeping up her spine to tell her she'd waited too long to
make her escape. Who but offshoots of the Donnelly
clan could have been blessed with such unruly cow-
licks, such thick black hair, such startlingly blue eyes?
The boys scrabbling at her feet were miniature replicas
of Joe, devils in the making. And if they were here,
could he be far behind?

CHAPTER TWO

"GIVE the lady her money, kids." Smooth and seductive as black satin, his voice practically stroked the back of her neck.

The boys could have robbed her of her last dollar for all Imogen cared. At that precise moment her only concern was that she not make a spectacle of herself. The last time she'd seen Joe Donnelly, she'd been an emotional mess. She would not appear the same way again. If anyone was to be caught at a disadvantage, it would be he.

Exercising an hauteur not even her mother could have matched, Imogen turned her head ever so casually and spared him a brief over-the-shoulder glance. "Oh, hello. It's Joe, isn't it?"

The effort was worth what it cost her, if only to witness the way his jaw dropped and his sultry black lashes spiked upward as the famous Donnelly eyes widened in shocked recognition.

"Imogen?" His voice changed, losing its baritone resonance and emerging rusty as a chunk of old metal fished from the depths of the lake.

"That's right." Even though her insides were churning, she flashed a cool, impersonal smile and tucked a few retrieved articles inside her bag. "Imogen Palmer. Patsy and I went to school together and were just reminiscing over old times."

"The hell you say!"

He sounded as if he were being strangled. If she

hadn't been in such pain, she might have enjoyed his discomfiture. Instead, since there was no other way for her to escape unless she chose to vault over the iron railing separating the patio from the park, she steeled herself to turn and face him.

Oh, he was beautiful! Contrary to all she'd told herself, he was as trim and fit a specimen of manhood as any woman could wish for. Despite the intensified gloom under the awning, she could see that his face was more chiseled than it had been when he was twenty-three, defining more fully the character of the man he'd become. He stood tall and proud, the rebel in him controlled but not tamed.

"Well," she said, turning away before he read the desolation she knew must show in her eyes, "it's been nice seeing you again, Patsy. Sorry we didn't have more time to chat."

Patsy looked from her to Joe, her expressive face betraying utter confusion. "But—"

One of the boys held out a grimy paw. "Here's your money, lady."

"Thank you," Imogen said, avoiding his clear-eyed gaze. She could not bear to look at him or his brother. Stepping past them and the man at their side, she said, "Sorry to rush off like this, Patsy, but we'll probably see each other again in the next day or so. Goodbye, Joe. You have lovely children."

She hoped she made a dignified exit. Spine straight, she tried to move with the unhurried grace of a fashion model through the maze of tables which wove an obstacle course between her and the gate. Only when she'd covered a hundred yards or so of her return journey along the shoreline boardwalk and was a safe distance from the restaurant did she allow herself to slump against the promenade wall and draw a shaking hand over her face.

Surprised, she found she was crying. Not with the great, harrowing, painful sobs she'd endured when Joe Donnelly had left her nine summers before. Not with the mourning hopelessness she'd known when she'd walked out of Colthorpe Clinic the following spring, her arms as empty as her heart. But silently, with tears flowing warm and unchecked down her cheeks.

Footsteps intruded on the silence, and again premonition shivered over her, warning her that escape was not to be so easily bought. A second later his voice, in control, bore out the fact. "Not so fast, Imogen."

Appalled, she fished a tissue out of her bag, swabbed at her tears and tried to blow her nose discreetly. "What is it?" she asked, grateful for the blessed camouflage of twilight. "Did I forget something?"

He touched her, placing his hand on her shoulder as if he were about to arrest her for loitering. "Apparently you did."

"Really?" Trying to shrug him off, she peered into her bag as intently as if she expected to find a snake hidden there. Anything was preferable to looking him in the eye. "What?"

"Us," he said, spinning her to face him. "Or did you hope I'd forgotten that Patsy wasn't the only Donnelly you were familiar with at one time?"

"He is immoral, insolent and socially unacceptable," her mother had raged when she'd learned Joe had brought Imogen home from her high school graduation dance. "Should he dare to set foot on this property again, I will have him arrested for trespassing."

But while he undoubtedly possessed more than his share of faults, unflinching honesty had been but one of Joe Donnelly's strengths, and he'd lost nothing of his penchant for confrontation. Where other men might have gone along with Imogen's pretense that they were nothing but the most casual of acquaintances, he was determined to challenge her on it.

"I hoped you'd be gentleman enough not to remind me," she said.

His voice hardened. "But I'm not a gentleman, Imogen. I never was. Surely you hadn't forgotten that?"

How did she answer? By confessing that simply seeing him again was enough to make her long for the feel of his mouth on hers? That it was suddenly too easy to look at the star-sprinkled sky and remember how, the night he'd loved her, the wash of the summer moon had turned his skin to pale gold? Or that, if she matched his truth with one of her own, she'd have to admit he was the most exciting man she'd ever met and he'd spoiled her for anyone else?

"How could I have forgotten?" she asked, overwhelmed by the vicious ache of memory. "A gentleman would have…"

He heard the unguarded desolation in her tone. "What?" he asked, his gaze scouring her face. "What would a gentleman have done that I didn't do?"

Found a way to stay in touch, she wanted to reply. *He'd have called or written or shown up at the door and refused to go away. He'd have been beside me when I needed him, and to hell with whether or not my mother approved. He'd have shared my grief. But you did none of those things because you didn't care.*

"It doesn't matter," she said. "Our...what happened between us that night..."

"Yes, Imogen? Exactly what did happen?"

He was taunting her, daring her to speak as bluntly as he did. Well, why not? Why should she step delicately, afraid to trample on his feelings, while he stomped roughshod over hers?

"We had sex, Joe. A one-night stand. The ice princess needed to learn what 'it' was really all about, and who better to teach her than the guy who'd already had every other willing girl in town? Is that what you want to hear?"

"No," he said, his hands falling from her as if he'd found he was touching slime. "I was hoping you'd tell the truth, for a change."

"You think I'm lying?"

He swung his gaze from her and stared across the darkening lake. "I never deluded myself about why you turned to me that night, Imogen. But even allowing for that, I still believed you came away from our—" he curled his lip scornfully "—encounter feeling better about yourself. So I hope to hell you *are* lying now."

"What does it matter either way, Joe? You obviously didn't lose much sleep over the whole business."

"Didn't I?"

A hundred yards or so ahead, the illuminated dome of the hotel reared into the night like a beacon. Why didn't she run toward the refuge it promised? Why did she let his question provoke her into having the last word and thereby reveal the misery she was feeling? "Well, you're married, aren't you?" she said, flinging the rebuke in his face. "You've got two children, both already in school, which explains how *you've* been keeping busy since the last time I saw you. I'd call that getting on with your life without wasting too much time on regrets.''

''And that upsets you, Imogen?''

''Not in the slightest,'' she said loftily, her bedraggled pride finally coming to the rescue. ''Why in the world would it?''

''I can't imagine,'' he said, a suggestion of sly humor in his voice. ''Especially since I'm neither married nor the father of those boys you met.''

''But Patsy said she's their aunt, which makes you—oh, dear!'' The laugh she manufactured to try to cover her embarrassment sounded pathetically like the bleating of a distraught sheep. ''How very silly of me.''

''Right,'' he said, so smugly she could have slapped him. ''I'm their uncle.''

''Well, it was a natural enough mistake on my part,'' she said, wishing she could disappear in a puff of smoke before she humiliated herself further. ''Sean was a year behind me in school. It never occurred to me he'd be the one to settle down and get married so young.''

''Wrong again, Imogen. He tied the knot with his high school sweetheart, Liz Baker, when they were nineteen, and Dennis was born six months later.''

She'd had one shock too many in the past hour. That was the only excuse she could offer for her next incredibly tactless remark. ''You mean, they *had* to get married?''

The look he turned on her, half pity and half disgust, made her cringe. ''We mortals who come from Lister's Meadows tend to make mistakes like that,

Imogen. Our animal appetites get the better of us—
not that I'd expect someone of your refined sensibili-
ties to understand that.''

Oh, she understood—more than he'd ever know!

But what good would it do to say so at this late
date? Casting about for an escape from a situation
growing more fraught with tension by the minute, she
saw they'd finally drawn level with the Briarwood's
entrance. Wanting nothing more than to rush up the
steps and disappear through the front doors, she forced
herself to observe the social niceties ingrained in her
from birth. ''Well, it was a pleasure seeing you, Joe,
and I've enjoyed catching up on all your news.
Perhaps we'll run into each other again some time.''

Any other man would have taken the hint, shaken
the hand she extended and left. Not Joe Donnelly. He
looked first at her hand, then at the floodlit facade of
the hotel, before zeroing in on her face with that too-
candid, too-observant gaze of his. ''Are you telling me
you're staying at the Briarwood or just trying to get
rid of me before someone you know sees the kind of
company you're keeping?''

''I'm staying at the hotel.''

''Why? What's wrong with staying at home?''

''My mother is away for a couple of days, and I
didn't want to put the staff out.''

''Why did she go away when she knew you were
coming?''

''Because—'' She stopped and drew a frustrated
breath. ''You ask too many questions, Joe Donnelly.''

''I guess that means you aren't going to let me buy
you a drink while you fill me in on what you've been
up to since we last saw each other?''

"Thank you, no. It's been a long day, and I'm rather tired."

"In other words, your life is none of my business."

She looked him straight in the eye. "As a matter of fact, it isn't."

He held her gaze an uncomfortably long time. "Fine. Sorry I bothered you. It won't happen again."

Then he did exactly what she'd wanted him to do—turned and strode back the way he'd come. Left her again, without so much as a backward glance. And she, fool that she was, felt her heart splinter a little, as if a piece of glass lodged there for years had suddenly broken loose.

Her strength seemed to drain out through the soles of her feet. She sank to the edge of the hotel lawn, afraid she was going to faint. Apparently, so did a couple who passed her. "Looks as if she's had one too many," the woman remarked, giving her a wide berth.

Imogen didn't care. She had only one thought, to hide herself behind the closed door of her room before she confronted the emotions sweeping through her. Not shock. She was past that. And not the thunderstruck notion that, after all these years, she was still in love with Joe Donnelly. That was so clichéd as to be laughable.

No, what terrified her was the feeling of having her back to the wall as destiny finally caught up with her. She had run for years. But in coming back to Rosemont, she had tempted fate too far, and it was about to demand a reckoning.

The phone was ringing as she let herself into her room. It was Tanya, calling for an update.

"You're overtired," she said, when Imogen tried to

describe the foreboding gripping her. "It's a long enough flight from Vancouver to Toronto, never mind the drive you had to face once you landed."

But Imogen remained unconvinced. She was realizing too late that it wasn't possible to dig up selective parts of the past. It was an all-or-nothing undertaking, and she hadn't bargained on that, at all.

Patsy was stretched out on the couch, watching the eleven o'clock news, when Joe got home. "Hi," she said, turning off the TV. "How was your evening?"

"Just peachy!" He flung himself down beside her and scowled at the blank screen. "Did you get the boys home okay?"

"Of course I got them home okay. What's put you in such a lousy mood?"

"I'm not in a lousy mood."

"You could have fooled me," she said, subjecting him to uncomfortably close scrutiny.

He squirmed under her gaze. "For Pete's sake, stop looking at me as if I've just broken out in spots! I'm not one of your patients."

She let the silence spin out for a while, then said, "I gather your hot date with Imogen didn't pan out."

"It wasn't a date."

"Gee, you could have fooled me. The way you went racing after her, anyone would think—"

"Can it, Patsy!"

Her voice softened. "I'm sorry. I didn't know she was that important to you."

"She's not." He slouched against the cushions and gazed at the ceiling. "It's just that some things never change, no matter how much time goes by. I wasn't good enough for Imogen Palmer in the old days and I should have known better than to think she'd spare me the time of day now. End of story.''

''I think you're selling both yourself and Imogen short. She was never a snob.''

''Don't give me that! You've only got to look at the way she was brought up by that mother of hers.''

''Dad drinks,'' Patsy pointed out, ''but that doesn't make us alcoholics.''

''I know.'' He blew out a sigh of frustration. ''But let's face it, Pats, the Imogen Palmers of this world stick to their own breed—corporate giants backed by old money.''

''From everything you've told me, you're not exactly subsisting on a pittance, either, Joe, and women have been falling at your feet ever since you started shaving. So what's this really all about?''

Guilt, that's what. And shame. But he wasn't about to open up that can of worms, not tonight and especially not with Patsy. ''Damned if I know,'' he said. ''Could be that she's involved with some other guy and not interested in shooting the breeze with—''

''She's not involved with anyone else. I know that for a fact because she told me so.''

''Well, that proves my point then, doesn't it? She'd rather be alone than spend any time with someone like me.''

Patsy gave him another of those annoyingly clinical looks. It stretched to a minute before, having finally arrived at some decision, she said, ''I shouldn't be telling you this and I wouldn't if you weren't the brother I adore despite his bullheadedness, but I happen to know that this 'goddess' of yours has feet of clay just like the rest of us. She didn't leave town suddenly the summer after we graduated because the air didn't agree with her—''

"I know," he said, cutting her off. "She went to some fancy finishing school in Switzerland, which also goes to prove my point."

"No, she didn't. She was pregnant, and her mother sent her to live with relatives somewhere down near the U.S. border so no one here would find out."

When he'd first begun working with horses, a young stallion had kicked him in the ribs, only a glancing blow, fortunately, but at the time Joe thought his chest had caved in. He felt the same way now. "It's not like you to spread ugly rumors, Pats."

"It's no rumor, Joe. To make a bit of extra money, I worked part-time for Dr. Rush and Dr. Stevens all summer, filing medical records, and I saw her chart."

Sweat prickled the pores of his skin. Patsy had never been a gossip. Was it likely she'd be passing on information if she wasn't sure of her facts?

Still, he continued to deny it. "You're mistaken," he said. "Or else you're mixing her up with someone else."

"No, I'm not."

"What makes you so sure? Plenty of girls get pregnant. Look at Liz."

"But not girls like Imogen Palmer, Joe. I mean, think about it. She hardly ever even dated, and when she did, the family chauffeur used to drive her and the boy to and from wherever they were going. Ian Lang bragged to everybody that the only reason he asked her out in grade eleven was so he'd get to ride in the back of that big black Mercedes."

"Ian Lang always was an ass."

"Yes." Patsy had that look again, and it was pointing straight at him—again. "I know you won't repeat what I've told you to anybody, Joe."

Wrong! There was one person he'd definitely be talking to.

"It's ancient history, after all, and no one else's business."

Wrong again, Pats!

"I only told you to rid you of this ridiculous inferiority complex you seem to have developed where Imogen's concerned."

"Yeah. Sure. Who gives a damn, anyway?"

He did! But he wasn't about to let Patsy know.

He made a big production of yawning. "I'm about ready to hit the sack."

"Me, too. Want anything before we turn in?"

He wanted plenty—answers, mostly, but he'd make do with a stiff belt of bourbon for now. "I'll pass, thanks. You go to bed, and I'll let Taffy out for a run before I come up."

The back porch lay deep in shadow. Moonlight glinted off the bottle of Jack Daniels perched on the railing. Leaning against one of the posts supporting the roof, with Taffy, the dog he'd found abandoned by the side of the road ten years ago, at his feet, Joe stared at the strip of garden and wondered how everything could possibly remain so utterly untouched by the turmoil raging inside him.

The sound of the courthouse clock striking midnight came faintly on the night air. Another nine hours at least before he could get any answers. How in hell was he supposed to fill the time between now and then?

Taffy stirred in her sleep, whimpered groggily and twitched her arthritic old legs at the phantom rabbits chasing through her dreams. He knew all about dreams. They were what had got him through the time he'd served in Pavillion Amargo, the jail he'd been sent to after Coburn's death.

They'd met when he'd signed on with the crew of a sailboat being brought from Ecuador to San Diego. Like everyone else on board, Joe had recognized Coburn for the brute he was, but the trouble began on Ojo del Diablo, a Caribbean island where they dropped anchor to pick up fresh supplies.

Coburn got in a drunken brawl and just about beat one of the locals to death. Joe stepped in to break things up, and Coburn fell and split his skull. Within minutes, the police were on the scene, he had blood on his hands, and there were two men lying in the gutter, one of them dead.

Justice, he'd soon learned, was pretty basic in little banana republics, especially when one of their own was involved. Before he knew it, he was in the slammer and the rest of the crew had set sail.

He survived the next months on memories of Rosemont Lake's clear, unpolluted water, on the smell of clean sheets dried in the sun on his mother's washing line, the taste of her apple pie still warm from the oven. Clichés every one, but they kept him from going mad.

And sometimes, when the moans of other prisoners filled the night, he dreamed of Imogen in a long white dress, and how she clung to him and wept in his arms, and how he'd made her smile again. He'd wondered if she remembered him, if he'd live to see her again, if there would ever be another time when she'd turn to him. But never, in his wildest imaginings, had he thought he might have left her pregnant.

Was that what he'd done? And if so, what had happened to the child?

He drained his glass, grabbed the bottle and stepped quietly to the end of the porch where the old hammock hung. It was going to be a long night. He might as well make himself comfortable.

Imogen was up and on the road by eight, her mind refreshed by sleep, her fears of the previous night washed away. It was seeing Joe Donnelly again that had done it. Being close enough to touch him. Of course she'd been shaken up. Who wouldn't be?

Still, she wasn't about to take a chance on running into him again. She read in the local paper of an estate auction at a farm near Baysfield, a small market town about two hours' drive away, and planned her escape.

She arrived in Rosemont just after four, half a dozen gorgeous quilts on the seat next to her, and went straight to Deepdene. Her mother answered the door. And even after all those years apart, the best she could come up with by way of welcome was to say plaintively, "Oh, it's you, Imogen."

Deciding such a tepid reception hardly warranted an offer to kiss her mother's delicately rouged cheek, Imogen said, "Yes, Mother. How are you?"

"Well, I'm...surprised. When Molly gave me your note, I hardly knew what to think."

Imogen suppressed a sigh. What had she expected? That the leading light of Rosemont society might have undergone a transformation and become suffused with such an uprush of maternal feeling she'd fling her arms around her only child and call for the fatted calf to be served for dinner? Hardly! On the other hand, the air of poised self-confidence that had been Suzanne's trademark was missing. She seemed diffident, nervous almost.

''Is it so surprising that, since I'm in town anyway, I should want to see you?'' Imogen asked gently.

''But why now, after so many years?''

''Because there are matters to put right between us, Mother, and I've...missed you.''

''Well,'' Suzanne said doubtfully, ''I suppose you'd better come in, then.''

CHAPTER THREE

IMOGEN followed her into the formal drawing room, where Suzanne always received visitors.

"Would you care for some tea, Imogen?"

"I'd love some. Do you still have it served in the sunroom?"

"My daily ritual." A small smile touched her mother's face. "How nice that you remember."

"Of course I do. It was quite a shock yesterday to find you'd broken the habit."

Suzanne got up and fidgeted with the triple string of pearls around her neck. "Yesterday I had...an appointment."

Imogen saw suddenly that the years had not been kind to her mother. In fact, she looked positively unwell. "Have you been ill, Mother?"

Affronted, Suzanne straightened her spine and cast Imogen a glare. "Certainly not. Why would you suppose such a thing?"

"You seem a little tired."

"I have been busy as, I am sure, have you." She tugged the bellpull hanging beside the fireplace. "I'll order tea, and you can tell me what you've been doing with yourself since you moved to the west coast. Are you still an interior decorator?"

"Yes," Imogen said, following her across the hall and into the huge solarium.

"I'd have thought," her mother said, perching on the edge of one of the sofas and crossing her still-elegant ankles, "that the trust fund from your father would have precluded the need for you to go out to work."

Her tone suggested that earning a living ranked only slightly above picking pockets.

"I like to be busy, Mother, and I enjoy the work."

"Do you own the company, dear?"

"No."

"How odd. I don't believe a Palmer has ever worked for someone else. But then, you've never behaved quite as I expected."

"Especially not the summer I graduated from high school."

The maid wheeled in a brass tea trolley just then, and Imogen knew from Suzanne's flared nostrils and raised brows that this particular topic of conversation was temporarily off-limits.

She waited until they were alone again before pursuing the one subject she was determined to discuss. "I'm sure you'd prefer that I not bring this up, Mother, but I think you and I need to talk about that time."

"Why would you want to dig up history best forgotten?"

"Because I lost more than a baby. I lost a mother, too. And you lost a daughter. And it strikes me as a terrible waste that we've let so much time go by without repairing the damage to our relationship." She looked around the vast room. "This used to be my home. It's part of me, of who I am. But this is the first time I've been back since you sent me to live with your cousin Amy."

"You could have come home again." Suzanne hesitated before adding, "Afterward."

"But I stayed away to punish you, Mother, because

for a long time I felt you had abandoned me when I needed you the most.''

"I did what I thought was best for you. What would you have had me do? Keep you here, where everyone knew you, and so make it impossible for you to go forward with your life without your past following wherever you went?''

"It followed me anyway. Mother. Or did you think I'd simply forget my little daughter?''

"I certainly hoped you would.''

"Did you forget me, Mother? Does any woman ever forget the child she gave birth to?''

"Really, Imogen!'' Suzanne set the sterling teapot on its stand with a decided clatter. "I find this conversation most upsetting and, to be perfectly frank, in very poor taste.''

"Yes,'' Imogen said, dismayed to find her mother could still hurt her. "I can see that you do. Perhaps I was wrong to think we could make amends. Perhaps there are things neither one of us can ever really forgive the other for.''

Agitation lent a hectic flush to Suzanne's cheeks. "That isn't so, at least not on my part. I'm happy to see you. If it's possible for us to start over, I'm willing to try. But I warn you now that it won't happen if you insist on harping on matters best left alone. That whole business is a closed book.''

"But it isn't for me! How can it be, when I never even saw my baby? One day I was pregnant, could feel her kicking inside me, and the next she was dead and gone, and I was expected to behave as if she'd never existed. Well, that isn't how it works, Mother. Before you and I can resume any sort of worthwhile relationship, I need to find closure, too.''

"Imogen, I'm begging you!" Ashen-faced, Suzanne put down her cup and saucer and raised ruby-tipped fingers to her temples.

Her mother looked ill, Imogen realized with sudden compunction. The late afternoon sun slanting cruelly across the fine patrician features revealed a pinched unhappiness about the eyes and mouth, the kind brought about by recurrent pain.

Fortunately, the maid came in. "Will there be one more for dinner, madam?"

"I'm afraid not," Suzanne said. "I feel one of my headaches coming on. I'm sorry, Imogen, but I'm going to have to go and lie down with a cold cloth over my eyes."

"Of course. Is there anything I can get for you? An aspirin, perhaps?"

"No, thank you. I have special migraine medication to take when this happens. Molly will help me."

The visit was clearly at an end. Collecting her things, Imogen prepared to leave. "Then I'll let myself out and call you tomorrow, if I may?"

"Of course."

Imogen hesitated, again tempted to embrace her mother. But when Suzanne got up from the sofa, she swayed on her feet, and it was obvious she really was in pain. Imogen touched her gently on the hand and said, "I'm sorry if my coming here has brought on this attack, Mother."

"I've brought it on myself, I'm afraid." She twisted the rings on her fingers and knit her finely arched brows as though wrestling with a dilemma. At length, she let out a long, defeated sigh, lifted her head and said in a low voice, "Won't you stay here while you're in town,

Imogen? I'd really like it very much if you would. I've...missed having a daughter all these years.''

It was the last admission Imogen had expected to hear. She could not believe how it moved her, or how, with so few words, so much healing could begin. Overwhelmed, she said, "I don't want to put you out, and the Briarwood is very comfortable.''

"But it's not your home, and if we are to find our way back to each other, surely the place to start is here under this roof where things went so terribly wrong to begin with.''

It was so much what she had hoped for that Imogen's throat ached. "Yes,'' she whispered, overcome. "Thank you, Mother.''

She was smiling as she drove from the house and humming by the time she drew up outside the hotel. "I'm checking out,'' she told the young man at the front desk. "Please have my bill ready and send someone for my luggage in half an hour.''

The clerk looked anxious. "Nothing's wrong, I hope, madam? No problem with our service?''

"No,'' she said, still all smiles. "Things couldn't be better.''

But they could deteriorate rapidly, she soon discovered. When a knock came at her door some twenty minutes later, she opened it, expecting it to be the bellhop arriving early. Instead, Joe Donnelly stood there, the light of battle sparking in his eyes.

"I'd invite me in, if I were you,'' he said, when she made no move to let him inside the room. "I don't think you're going to want the entire floor to know why I'm here.''

If she hadn't been taken so completely by surprise, Imogen would have told him she wasn't interested in finding out the reason for his unannounced visit, either, and shut the door in his face. Common sense demanded that, at the very least, she tell him to wait for her downstairs in one of the public rooms. Sheer self-preservation told her to refuse to see him at all. And ordinarily, Imogen listened to her instincts. But one look at Joe's face told her this was no ordinary occasion.

Last night, dusk had hidden what the clear light of day revealed. He had lost his old devil-may-care expression a long time ago. Any vestige of softness his mouth might once have shown was gone. His eyes, though as vividly blue as ever, possessed a wariness Joe Donnelly at twenty-three hadn't known.

He had always been ready to take on the world, secure in the belief that he was invincible, but the arrogance of youth had given way to a cynicism ready to flare into anger at the slightest provocation. And somehow, she had provoked him to anger now.

"What do you want?" she asked, backing away from him, allowing him into the room.

He followed, closing the door behind him. "Looks as if I got here just in time," he said, ignoring her question and jerking his head at the suitcase lying open on the bed. "I see you're getting set to run away again."

"I'm not running anywhere, Joe Donnelly. I'm staying with my mother for the rest of the time I'm here—not that I owe you any explanations."

"Oh, but you do, Imogen," he said, stalking her across the room until the backs of her knees hit the edge of the bed and made further retreat impossible. "And you can start by telling me why you skipped town so hurriedly just weeks after we had sex, the year you graduated from high school."

We had sex. Even though she'd flung the same callous

words at him the night before, having them hurled back at her now stung worse than salt in a newly opened wound. On the other hand, given his present mood, what else did she expect? That he'd couch his anger in euphemisms?

"I'm waiting," he said, looming over her. "Why the rapid exit from Rosemont, Imogen?"

"That's none of your business."

He folded his arms across his chest and planted his feet more firmly on the carpet, a statement that he'd allow nothing to deflect his purpose. "As of right now, I'm making it my business."

She didn't like the way he seemed to suck the oxygen out of the air. Even less did she like the way he intimidated her. There was something almost sinister in his velvet tone of voice, so at odds with the hard line of his mouth and the absolute coldness in his eyes.

"I'm waiting," he said, still with chilling softness.

She swallowed, scrambling to find an answer that would satisfy him and put an end to the inquisition. "I went to Switzerland for a year," she said, stretching the truth by a few months. "To school."

He moved suddenly, circling her wrists with his long, strong fingers and hauling her to her feet. "Liar! You had a baby. My baby."

The blood drained from her face, leaving her light-headed with shock. The Joe Donnelly she'd known and worshipped would never have cornered her so mercilessly, but this man was a stranger.

"Didn't you?" Imprisoning both her wrists in one hand, he grasped her chin in the other and forced her to meet his scrutiny.

Mutely, she stared at him, her silence an admission of guilt. There was a time she'd have welcomed being held by him, so close she could see the faint stippling of new beard growth on his jaw. But not like this, with his eyes blazing in his face and his mouth twisted with rage. As if his rights as a human being, as a man, had been violated.

Not as if, her conscience scolded. *His rights have been violated, pure and simple. He learned from someone else a truth he should have heard from you years ago.*

It was true, and looked at from his point of view, she knew her omission was inexcusable. "How did you find out?" she croaked, too dismayed to consider prevaricating.

"By accident."

"I'm sorry." She sounded as feebleminded as she felt.

"For what?" he bellowed. "For the way I found out I'd fathered a child, or that I found out at all? And don't try telling me it's none of my business then try to shoo me away, because it isn't going to happen, Imogen."

How he must despise her! "I'm sorry you had to find out like this," she mumbled.

"You could have prevented it. You could have told me yourself, at the time."

"I—"

"Let me guess why you didn't." The contempt in his tone seared her. "Donnelly genes didn't measure up to what it takes to be a Palmer heir. It was easier to write the whole thing off as an accident. Erase the mistake before anyone found out about it. How am I doing so far, princess? Batting a hundred?"

Too floored to refute such a ludicrous allegation, she stared at him. She'd opened her Pandora's box so carefully. How had this secret escaped? Who could have told him, when the only people in town who knew were her mother and the family doctor?

"I always thought your mother was a bitch," he said savagely, "but I never wanted to believe you were cut from the same cloth. I never thought you capable of cold-blooded murder."

"Stop it!" She choked the words out, stirred by the unfairness of his accusation and his unjustified attack on Suzanne.

"What else would you call abortion? You curled your aristocratic lip last night when you realized Sean and Liz had to get married, as you so prettily phrased it, but at least they didn't take the easy way out and flush a child, rather than have it screw up their long-term plans."

"I didn't, either!" she cried, hurt beyond measure that he'd leap to such a conclusion. But the ugly fact was, he'd made love to a stranger out of pity. He knew *of* her—that she belonged to the richest family in town, that she vacationed in the Alps and on the Riviera, had servants to cater to her needs and rode around town in the back of a chauffeur-driven limousine. But he'd never known *her,* the person she was inside. How could he be expected to understand what her reaction to the pregnancy might have been? "I didn't have an abortion," she said quietly. "I never even considered it."

It was his turn to be rendered speechless. Eventually, after a silence that thrummed with tension, he said, "Then what the hell happened to my child?"

"She died, Joe." The words fell into the room like marbles hitting glass. Their echo seemed to hang in the air forever.

"*What?*" His horrified gaze burned holes in her. "How?"

"She was stillborn."

The breath rushed out of him. "Stillborn?" he repeated hollowly, slumping into a chair.

Witnessing his shock was like reliving her own when she'd first been told. The tears welled up, and she felt again that clutching emptiness no amount of sympathy or kindness had been able to fill. How her soul had ached during those terrible days.

And how his was hurting now! "Why?" he asked, in that shell-shocked voice.

"Don't you think I've asked myself that over and over again? Why my baby? Why me?" And because he'd judged her so harshly to begin with, she asked, "And why you? Why not a man who cared enough for me to be by my side, to share the grief?"

If only he'd reach out to her then, how willingly she'd have gone to him. They had lost a child—surely the greatest sorrow any two people could be asked to bear—and should have been able to draw comfort and strength from each other.

But he did not. Instead, he swung his head in a slow arc, and she saw that his eyes had turned a winter-sky blue, the kind that comes after a blizzard, so hard and remote that she wondered if there was a spark of warmth or tenderness left in him.

"If I had known, I would have been there," he said. "But I did not know. You chose not to let me know."

"You left town," she said, "and since you didn't bother to say goodbye first, I took that as a clear message that you weren't interested in keeping in touch."

"So you thought you'd punish me by keeping knowledge of my child from me? Or was it more a case of hushing up the whole business entirely so that no one would know you'd rolled in the hay with a peasant?"

His first question gave her pause. She *had* been angry with him once the initial hurt of his desertion had subsided. It had been the only way she could cope. But his second accusation made her blush with shame.

She'd couched it in more refined terms, of course, but Suzanne's assessment had matched his. "Word of this cannot leak out," she'd declared. "That anyone should learn of a Palmer giving birth to a Donnelly bastard is insupportable. I will not hear of it! It would ruin our fine family name!"

Too heartsick to fight and too afraid of what the future held, Imogen the girl had gone along with her mother's edict. She'd packed her bags and disappeared without a trace. Why not? Joe Donnelly had long since done the same thing, heading west on his beloved Harley-Davidson and leaving nothing behind but a cloud of dust.

Still, Imogen, the woman, had to set the record straight. "I never—"

"Don't bother denying it," Joe cut in. "Your face says it all."

Conscience-stricken, Imogen turned away, knowing she'd left it eight years too late to expect him to believe his being the father would have been reason enough for her to have adored their child.

Her action seemed to infuriate him. Surging to his feet, he let fly with a string of curses and strode to the French window. She held her breath, anticipating another outburst. When one wasn't forthcoming, she ventured another look at him.

He stood with his back to her, one hand braced against the wall. The sun, half-hidden behind the branches of a tree, haloed his bowed head and the stiff, unyielding line of his shoulders. The atmosphere hummed with anger and suspicion.

Just when Imogen thought she could bear the tension

no longer, another knock came at the door. "Bellhop, Ms. Palmer."

She could not respond. Could not, if her life had depended on it, have navigated the stretch of carpet between her and the door. She was shaking. Shaking and empty and sick with useless regrets.

Finally, Joe went over and opened the door. "Take the bags," he told the man, passing him a tip, "and have Ms. Palmer's car brought to the front. She'll be down in a couple of minutes."

When they were alone again, he went into the bathroom and brought back a glass of water. "Here," he said.

"No." Feebly, Imogen tried to slap him away.

He didn't budge. "Drink it, Imogen. You're in no shape to get behind the wheel of a car in your present condition, and I've got enough on my conscience without your adding to it by driving off the road and winding up wrapped around a tree."

"I'd think you'd be glad if I did," she said, his unexpected concern undermining her even more thoroughly than his rage. The tears swam in her eyes, clogged her throat.

"That goes to show how little you know me. I happen to place a very high value on human life."

He was right again. She no more knew him than he knew her. But she hadn't let that stop her from judging him and finding him wanting. "I'm afraid I owe you a very great apology."

"You owe me a hell of a lot more than that, Imogen," he said flatly. "And you can be sure I intend to collect, very soon."

She had no doubt he meant every word. "Then I'll give you a call once I've settled in at home," she said.

*   *   *

So often when she'd been young, she'd seen Deepdene as a prison, its high stone walls a barricade between her and the life she longed to enjoy. But that night, when the gates at the main entrance swung closed behind her, it struck her for the first time as a refuge.

Once again, the maid Molly opened the door, this time with a smile. "Madam has retired for the night, but she hopes you'll join her for breakfast tomorrow, Miss Imogen."

Just as well. She'd had enough confrontation for one night.

Molly bent to pick up the suitcase. "If you'll follow me, I'll show you upstairs. Your old room's ready."

"Don't bother," Imogen said, forestalling her. "I know the way."

So much had remained the same on the main floor that she didn't expect to find changes upstairs. Still, it came as a shock when she opened the door at the end of the hall and stepped into the room she'd occupied from the time she was born until just after her eighteenth birthday.

Nothing had been touched. Absolutely nothing. The same blossom-sprigged paper covered the walls. The same Savonerie rug lay on the oak floor. The four-poster bed with its embroidered cotton canopy and cover; the books and photographs, the equestrian trophies, her old stuffed teddy bear—all were exactly as she'd left them. Even her writing materials sat on the desk under the window in the alcove as if she'd just stepped out for a moment before finishing a letter to a friend.

Leaving her luggage by the door, she went into the adjoining bathroom. Her favorite soap, bath oil and body powder were neatly arranged on the broad deck surrounding the soaker tub. Her favorite shampoo hung in the glass-enclosed shower. Her monogrammed towels hung from the brass rail. A half-empty bottle of the perfume she'd favored as a teenager stood in the mirrored cabinet above the washbasin, along with a pale pink lipstick and an opened tube of toothpaste, for heaven's sake!

A chill touched her, tiny, ghostlike fingers creeping over her skin. Uneasily, she backed into the bedroom and eyed the wardrobe on the far wall, the chiffonier beside the fireplace, the cedar chest at the foot of the bed.

A morbid fascination drew her toward them. She pulled open the drawers, swung open the doors. And found more relics of a girl who no longer existed.

Frilled baby-doll pyjamas for summer, full-length combed-cotton nightgowns with tucked yokes and long sleeves for winter. Cashmere sweaters and pleated skirts. A fourteen-year-old's first evening gown of pale blue crepe with a wide velvet sash. And in the mirror on the back of the wardrobe door, a woman staring at her, a stranger intruding on a shrine to a girl who'd ceased to exist a long time ago.

"Why?" she whispered, and the word seemed to bounce back at her from every surface.

She'd thought her mother would have had all traces of her removed, if not the furniture then at least the accessories, the clothes, the mementoes. But even her first corsage, pink roses from the boy who'd been her escort to the winter ball the year she'd worn the blue dress, had been preserved under a glass-domed display stand.

Laying her suitcase on the bed, she hauled out her clothes as though their presence could banish the ghosts of the past. Chic, sleek styles in subtle shades of plum and orchid and pearl gray. Softly tailored blouses and loose-fitting skirts. A black linen sheath and an ivory blazer with a matching straw boater for the retirement ceremony taking place in two days' time. A black silk two-piece suit in case she needed something dressy for evenings.

With one sweep of the hand, she consigned the girl's clothes to the back of the wardrobe and made room for the woman's outfits. With equal dispatch, she dumped the contents of two drawers onto the bed and replaced them with the things she'd need during her stay—silk lingerie trimmed with French lace, smoke-gray panty hose and two handbags, one of butter-soft Italian leather for daytime and a beaded clutch purse for evenings.

Gathering the items discarded from the drawers, she flung them into the cedar chest at the foot of the bed, stuffing them on top of old photo albums and bundles of greeting cards tied in ribbon she'd saved during her teens. And in doing so, she discovered the five-year diary she'd received on her fifteenth birthday. The cover was cream leather with an embossed gold border grown a little worn at the edges because it had seen a lot of wear and held the secrets of another lifetime.

She made the mistake of touching it, of picking it up and running her fingers over the smooth, cool leather. As if it had suddenly become a live thing, the book fell open at the first page, at which the girl she wanted so desperately to forget came back with a vengeance, bringing with her a whole host of memories, of heartache and heartbreak.

And the woman she'd become accepted what she'd known all along. There was no turning away from the past. The only way to defeat it was to face it.

CHAPTER FOUR

June 25

Dear Diary, Today's my fifteenth birthday and you're the first gift I opened. I'm having a pool party this afternoon and for the first time I get to ask friends from school for a change instead of girls I hardly know from the country club or equestrian center whose mothers are friends of my mother. (I think there's supposed to be a comma in there somewhere, but this isn't for anyone else to read so who cares.) Also, I've been begging for a two-piece swimsuit for ages and Mother's finally agreed to buy one for me. Yeah! No more boring one-piece things that went out of fashion in the last century.

June 26

Dear Diary, the party was the pits. I wanted to die at the way Mother looked at my friends as if she thought they were going to steal the silver. After everyone left, she told me most of the girls were too common to associate with a Palmer. Also my two-piece looked gross and might as well have been a one-piece, it covered so much. When Julie Coombs saw me in it, she just about split a gut laughing. I wish Patsy Donnelly could have been here, but when I mentioned her name, Mother put her foot down. "People from Lister's Meadows aren't our kind of people," she said—whatever that's supposed to mean.

August 17

Dear Diary, Guess what! Dave Baxter asked me out on a date! He asked me if I wanted to go to the movies with him on Friday. I said sure, but I don't know how I'm going to persuade Mother to let me go.

August 18

Dear Diary, I'm allowed to go to the movies with Dave but only if there's a crowd of us. So I phoned around and arranged it. The only problem is that Arthur, our chauffeur, has to deliver me and pick me up after. Also I have a ten o'clock curfew, but it's a beginning, right?

August 22

Dear Diary, Well, here it is, the biggest day of my life, and already my mother's ruined it. I started getting ready about an hour ago, shampooed my hair and stuff, then tried some of the blue eye shadow Debbie gave me for my birthday. I was all set to go when Mother showed up and made me wash my face and change out of my jeans because no daughter of hers was going out in public dressed like a tramp. So here I am, wearing a navy skirt and white sweater and looking like some fifties pom-pom girl, with my hair tied up in a ponytail and my nose so shiny you could see your face in it. Honestly!

August 23

Dear Diary, Dave Baxter is a disgusting creep. Halfway through the movie he suddenly attacked and tried to kiss me. I could feel his teeth. Worse, he had garlic pizza for dinner. Yuck! For once it didn't bother me that Arthur was parked outside the movie theater, waiting to drive me home. The way some of the girls at school talk about it, you'd think being kissed by a boy was a big deal but I can definitely live without it. Maybe I'll become a nun.

INSTEAD, she'd learned there was a huge difference between boys and men and allowed her fascination for Joe Donnelly to lead her down the primrose path to ruin! Was it possible she'd once been so young, so deliciously shocked by harmless vices and so filled with impossibly high expectations?

She was at the point of reading further when the phone rang, its double tone signaling that a call from the outside had come through on the house line and was being transferred to her room. Probably Tanya checking in for an update before she went out for the evening, Imogen thought, lifting the receiver. It was coming up to seven o'clock on the west coast.

But it was Joe Donnelly, the slight echo chasing his words indicating he was calling from a cell phone. "I'm at the back gates," he said, dispensing with preliminaries. "I want to see you."

She sat up so abruptly that the diary slid to the floor. "What, now, at this time of night?"

"I wasn't planning on camping out till morning, Imogen. And it's only just after ten, in case you haven't noticed. Hardly the witching hour."

"But I only just got here."

"So? There's no law that says you can't go out again, is there? Or do you still need Mother's permission to set foot outside the front door?"

Perhaps if she hadn't just read the diary, his barb wouldn't have found such an easy mark. But the memory of the control her mother had wielded over every aspect of her teenage years remained suffocatingly vivid.

"All right," she said, annoyed to find herself whispering and looking furtively toward the door as if afraid she might be caught consorting with the enemy. "I'll be down in fifteen minutes."

"Make it ten, and bring a jacket," he said, then hung up.

No goodbye, or thanks, or sorry if I disturbed you. Just an autocratic click in her ear. Yet she could no more have ignored his summons than she could have burned the diary.

Downstairs, a lamp burned on the carved table near the passage to the kitchen, but there was no sign of activity as she crossed the hall to the solarium and let herself out one of the big sliding windows on the west wall. From there, a flight of steps descended to the path that wound past the lily pond to the walled garden.

The moon was almost full, marking the route clearly. Not that she'd have had trouble if it had been pitch-black. She could have found her way blindfolded. The garden, over fifty acres of it, had been her refuge when she was young, a place of peace and solitude—and, for one unforgettable night, a place of magic.

Surefooted, she made her way to the south end of the property where the greenhouses stood. Only once did she falter, when she came to the glade where the little thatch-roofed cottage that had been her playhouse nestled under the low-hanging boughs of an ancient oak.

How ironic that the same moon that had watched her then lit the way for her now as she hurried to meet the man who'd stolen her innocence and broken her heart here in this secret, silent place. Was it an omen, a sign that some things never change and some mistakes are destined to be repeated?

Not if she had a brain cell to call her own, it wasn't!

And yet, hadn't she already learned how little sway her head held where Joe Donnelly was concerned? The sight and sound of him were enough to send her heart spinning. She knew it, knew the danger of him, and yet, when he called, she went running, and common sense be damned.

He was waiting in the lee of the wall outside the chief gardener's lodge where the shadows were deepest. "Good thing you remembered the jacket," he said and, taking her elbow, led her up the road to where the gleam of moonlight on black metal revealed a motorcycle propped next to a tree.

He handed her a helmet and checked to make sure the strap fit snugly beneath her chin before putting on his own. "Climb aboard," he said, swinging his leg over the saddle of the bike.

What was it that held her in such thrall that she obeyed him with the docility of a lamb being led to the slaughter? The warmth of his body, perhaps, and the summer-night scent of his skin? The ripple of muscle beneath his shirt as he rolled the bike into the middle of the road and turned eastward, away from Rosemont? Or was she driven by the secret, shameful, totally illogical hope that, if history was destined to repeat itself, this time they'd get it right?

Swifty, they roared toward open country, man and machine angling as one into the curves of the road as it looped around the deserted rim of the lake. And just as swiftly, Imogen was transported to the other time—the only time—the breadth of his body had shielded her from the air rushing past and the warmth of him had chased away the chills shaking her and she had wished they could ride without stopping until Rosemont and everything her life had been up until that moment was left behind forever.

Of course, it didn't happen, not then and not now. The moment of reckoning arrived, heralded by the motorcycle's snarling deceleration as Joe geared down and cruised along a rough path, which ended on a strip of rocky beach.

Low-rising hills enclosed this end of the lake, narrowing it to a lonely, deserted place restored to sudden, deafening silence as the engine died. Not a breath of air rippled the silvered surface of the water. Not a bird stirred.

Even Joe had lost some of his urgency and seemed content to remain slouched astride the motorcycle and gaze blankly at the scene before him. But since there was no earthly reason for her to remain plastered to his spine with her arms wrapped around his waist, she dismounted and removed her helmet.

Picking her way over the rocks, she said, "How peaceful it is here." A blatantly inaccurate observation, given the circumstances! The tension that had charged the atmosphere in the hotel room that afternoon continued to swirl between them.

She felt obligated to continue babbling, as though, if she distracted him with mindless chatter, he might forget the reason he'd brought her here. "I'm surprised people haven't snapped up the land and built summer retreats here. The water is so clear, and the view—"

His voice cut across her trite meanderings as cleanly as a scalpel slicing through flesh. "Purely as a matter of interest, what had you planned to do with the baby, had she lived?"

Although the question caught her off guard, at least

she was on sure ground with her answer. "There was never any doubt in my mind. I'd have kept her."

"And would you have bothered to contact me at that point? Enlisted my help?" he asked, continuing to focus on the lake.

"What does it matter? Our baby died, so the question never arose."

"I'll tell you why it matters," he said, climbing off the bike and spearing her with a look so loaded with pain that she flinched. "Because I was her father and I want to know. Because I have a *right* to know! You might have closed the book on her, but I've only just opened it. So whether you like it or not, Imogen, our association isn't going to end until I'm satisfied I've read every chapter."

Predator in pursuit of victim, he strode to where she hovered like a cornered animal at the edge of the water. "And forget harping on the business of my having left no forwarding address when I skipped town," he went on, stabbing his forefinger in her direction for emphasis, "because it just won't wash. There was never a time my family didn't know how to reach me. All you ever had to do was go to them and ask."

On the surface, his words were laced with bitter anger. But his eyes told a different tale, one of grief, of having been robbed of a part of himself. Like her, he'd lost a child. The difference was, he hadn't had years to adjust to the bereavement.

"I can't change the past, Joe," she said gently, knowing that simply to apologize was like offering a Band-Aid to a man suffering a heart attack. "All I can do is try to make you understand how it was for me and why I acted the way I did."

"I'm listening."

"I was trapped and didn't know where to turn. If you recall, that night—"

"It's hardly something I'm likely to forget."

It wouldn't have surprised her if he'd denied remembering any of it. She hadn't been the first girl he'd made love to, nor the last, and she doubted he'd found the experience particularly memorable. "Yes, well, although I'd hoped to sneak into the house undetected, I got no farther than the front door before my mother accosted me. If I'd been thinking straight at the time, I'd have realized she'd be there, waiting for me to show up."

"How so?"

"Our chauffeur had driven into town to pick me up from the dance two hours before, only to find I'd already left, and of course he reported as much to her, so she knew full well something was amiss. And just to clinch matters, when I finally did show up, I was wearing your leather jacket over my dress."

"Did you explain why?"

She let out a strangled sigh. "I tried. Said I'd borrowed it because I chilled. But my face, my hair, the hem of my dress, my shoes—they were in complete disarray. One glance, and my mother knew exactly what I'd been up to."

"Some mother you've got!"

"And some daughter she had! I knew what she wanted me to say—that I was ashamed, repentant—and I just couldn't do it. Because despite all that had happened earlier in the evening, what I most felt at that moment was...cherished."

At that, his lashes swept down to shield his emotions, but not before she saw how her confession had touched him. Almost savagely, he picked up a flat stone and sent it skipping over the water, shattering the mirrored surface into a dazzling explosion of light and shadow.

"The one thing I couldn't pretend was regret," she said, "and that enraged her. She was not used to being opposed by anyone, least of all the daughter who'd always submitted to her authority and of whom she expected such high moral standards. She saw my defiance as the ultimate betrayal."

"Made worse, no doubt, by the fact that, of all the people you could have turned to for help, you chose me."

"That didn't improve matters, no, especially since, for all your professed concern for my safety, you didn't care enough to follow it up with so much as a phone call to make sure I was none the worse for my misadventure."

He stared at her in blank amazement and opened his mouth as if to refute what she'd said. Then, seeming to think better of the idea, he snapped his jaw closed.

After a moment, Imogen picked up the thread of her story. "She read the riot act, pointing out that one had only to look at me to know I'd cheapened a great family name with my wanton behavior, that if word of my escapade ever got out, she'd never again be able to lift her head in decent society, that it was as well my father wasn't alive because what I'd done would surely have killed him and that she'd make sure I didn't disgrace her again with my sin-filled ways."

Joe choked back a laugh. "She actually used those words?"

But the memories she'd revived were too painful for Imogen to find them amusing. It had taken a very long time for her to shed the miserable legacy of that evening. "More or less."

"And how did you defend yourself?"

"Believe it or not, I was more concerned with figuring out a way to meet you again and return your jacket."

"The jacket wasn't important, Imogen," he said quietly.

"It was to me," she told him, remembering how she'd hugged it to her during that long night, drawing comfort from the heavy silk lining and the mingled scent of leather and whatever shaving lotion he'd used. "But I realized the odds against my sneaking away to meet you the next night as we'd planned were slim to nonexistent, so I left a note in the pocket, explaining I had to break our date, then took the jacket to the cottage early the next morning before anyone was up."

"I know. I found it when I went back that evening."

She waited for him to add something, to offer an excuse for not having bothered to try to see her when the fuss had died down. Instead, he stooped and sent another stone skimming across the lake. Only after it sank did he straighten and say, "What did she do next? Drag you to a doctor and force him to examine you to verify the worst?"

"No. She shipped me off to Paris for a month, ostensibly to polish my French but in reality to remove me from the scene of further temptation."

"If you didn't like the idea, why did you go along with it? Did it never occur to you to stand up to her and tell her that it was your life and you'd damned well live it the way you saw fit?"

"At the time," she replied, stung by the scorn he made no attempt to hide, "it was all I could do to get from one day to the next without falling apart. I'd been through a pretty traumatizing experience, in case you've forgotten."

"Yeah, well..." His glance slid away and settled on

the distant hills. "As you said earlier, you can't go back and change the past."

She knew then he'd never had the slightest intention of pursuing the relationship. What she had perceived as the beginning of something wonderful hadn't been anything more than a one-night stand for him, one he'd have preferred to avoid if he'd had the chance.

"You never really cared about me, did you, Joe?"

"I was there when you needed rescuing, wasn't I?"

"Yes. But you'd have done the same for anyone."

"Not quite, Imogen. I like to think I'm civilized enough to defend a woman without expecting her to reward me with her sexual favors."

"Then what made me so attractive all of a sudden? You'd seen me around town before and never shown any interest in pursuing me."

"I was five years older than you, for crying out loud! And even if the age difference hadn't mattered, you were hardly the girl next door. You don't need me to point out that we had nothing in common."

"That doesn't answer my question. What made that night different?"

"Damned if I know how to put it in words." He shrugged helplessly. "You were so fine, so...fragile. I thought you were going to break. And I wanted to hold you together somehow."

"Are you saying you felt sorry for me?"

He looked at her, his eyes somber in the night. "Yes."

She recoiled before his bluntness. "Oh!" she whispered, and spun away before he saw how his reply had wounded her. She had given him everything. *Everything!* Her heart, her body, her soul. And all he'd been able to offer her in return was his pity.

He came up behind her and placed his hand on her shoulder. "Look, I wasn't trying to hurt you then and I'm not trying to hurt you now. I'm being honest. Isn't that what this evening's all about, telling each other the truth?"

"Yes," she said, shrugging off his touch. "And now that we have, I see no need to prolong things. If you don't mind, I'd like to go home."

He might never have betrayed a moment's concern for her feelings. "I do mind, princess. You're only half-way through your story, and I haven't begun to give my account, so finish what you started, unless you want to spend the rest of the night out here."

She stared at him mutinously.

He folded his arms and stared back. "I'm waiting, Imogen."

"There's nothing more to tell. I got pregnant. When my mother found out, she shipped me off to stay with her second cousin."

"Where?"

"What does it matter?" she asked bitterly. "It's enough that I wasn't walking around Rosemont sticking out a mile in front and shaming her in front of her golfing friends and bridge partners at the club."

"*Where,* Imogen?"

She spat out the words like bullets. "Ferndale, a little town near Niagara Falls. I stayed there for the pregnancy, went into labor on February the eighteenth and gave birth on the nineteenth. As soon as I was well enough to travel, I picked up where I'd left off before I so inconsiderately got myself in trouble and went to school in Switzerland for a year. I never came back to Rosemont."

"Why not?"

"There was nothing to come back to, except a lot of unhappy reminders. I decided to see the world instead. I'd done Europe already, so I traveled to the Far East and New Zealand, then made my way back to Canada and settled in Vancouver, where I've lived ever since. End of story."

"What brought you here now?"

"Miss Duncliffe's retirement—and the hope that I could establish some sort of adult relationship with my mother."

"Why? You say she felt you betrayed her, but it seems to me the shoe's on the other foot. Where was she when you needed her?"

"Where were you?" Imogen challenged. "Don't you see? You're the only one who could have made a difference. If you'd been there—"

"Are you suggesting it's my fault the baby died?"

"I don't know. Maybe. Who's to say how much my state of mind during the pregnancy might have affected the health of my baby?" She was crying and didn't care—not that he was seeing her at her worst or that what came spilling out of her mouth served no purpose except to hurt him as he'd hurt her. "Maybe she knew her father didn't want her so she just didn't bother to live."

"Imogen!"

She heard the dismay in his voice and spun away, embarrassed to hear herself sobbing uncontrollably but unable to stop it. She hadn't wept like that in over eight years, not since the day she'd walked out of the clinic in Ferndale feeling more alone and unloved than any human being ever should. Having found a crack in the dam of her defenses, all the grief she'd repressed for so long rose up and poured through, overwhelming her.

"Leave me alone," she wailed. "Go away!"

"Sure," he crooned, his hands gentle on her shoulders. "Whatever you say, princess."

But instead of letting her go, he turned her around, cupped her face between his palms and with the ball of both thumbs trapped the tears pooling along her lashes and streaming down her cheeks. And then he closed his mouth over hers and stopped her sobs with a kiss.

The pressure of his lips was light, soothing, comforting. A friend's kiss. Slowly, the hard lump of misery inside her melted. Her fists unclenched against the solid warmth of his chest. The aching tension drained out of her throat, leaving her neck as supple as a daisy stem bending in a breeze.

But then everything changed. Imperceptibly, the way mist can creep up to obscure all the sharp, clear lines of a scene until the view becomes blurred and softened, his embrace crossed the boundary separating friend from lover.

He slid his fingers away from her face to trace her throat and the angle of her collarbone. His knee nudged her legs apart, a subtle, persuasive invitation. One arm swept around her waist. And the kiss that had begun so quietly rose to a thundering crescendo, wild and insatiable.

She should have expected what came next. It was not, after all, her first experience with him. The combination of summer scents, shadows and Joe Donnelly looming tall and dark against her took potent effect. Helpless to fend off the heat coiling within her, she leaned into him, swayed against him.

Her arms found their way around his neck. Her fingers buried themselves in his hair. So silky it was, so soft and thick. And he was so...hard.

The heat shot through her, liquid satin, sapping her of the will to resist, intent only on sheathing his strength. What might she have done if he had not put an end to things?

She knew and was horrified. At eighteen, she could blame her innocence. At twenty-seven, she could blame only herself. If he had not pulled away and held her firmly at arm's length, she would have sunk down with him at the water's edge where the rocks gave way to powder-fine sand and she would have made love with him. She would have risked everything again just for the fleeting ecstasy of being possessed by him one more time. Oh, God, would she never learn?

But he had learned all too well. Thrusting her away, he said, his voice like gravel, "I'm taking you home. Now."

When she sagged against him, deflated, demoralized, he caught her in his arms, strode to the bike and plunked her on the pillion as if she were a wilful, disobedient child being banished to the naughty chair.

"Put this on," he said, shoving the helmet at her, and before she'd had time to collect herself, he was revving the engine as if he intended to soar clear of the earth and deposit her on some far-flung planet.

Too soon, they were at Deepdene and he was towing her past the greenhouses and along the path beside the vegetable gardens, so anxious to be rid of her that it was all she could do to keep pace with him. Until he came into the glade where the cottage stood, and then he stopped dead, apparently mesmerized by the sight of the moon-dappled path leading to the front door.

"Remember this place?" she taunted softly. She couldn't help herself. Once upon a time, those walls had closed around them and shut out the ugliness. Under the protection of that roof, they'd made magic out of may-hem—together. Two hearts, two bodies, two souls. How could he claim to have been motivated solely by compassion?

"I remember," he said, dropping her hand as if it were a live coal and wheeling away from her. "You can find your own way from here."

Wraithlike, he merged with the shadows and within seconds had disappeared. But the feel of his arms around her, the touch of his mouth on hers, lingered, kept alive by the surge of emotion that had flared between him and her. He could protest all he liked, but out there on that beach, when he had kissed her and held her, it had not been because he felt sorry for her. Her experience might be limited, but she knew enough to recognize the signs of a man tormented by passion and driven by desire. The racing heart, the labored breath, the proud thrust of masculine flesh—they weren't conjured by sympathy. For a few delirious moments, he had wanted her.

As for herself—oh, she was a mess! It was one thing to realize that facing up to memories was the only way to strip them of their power. But he had pushed her one step further and made her see that the careful, no-risk, no-pain adult life she'd built for herself was just as much a prison as the claustrophobic confines of Deepdene had been when she was growing up. And without meaning to, he'd once again come to her rescue and set her free. Free to feel, to care, to hunger. To love.

Why was it, she wondered, wending her way to the house, that of all the men she knew, he was the only one who could ease the starving, empty places in her heart? Why not someone easy and straightforward instead of this difficult, unpredictable, untamable man?

It was after midnight when she let herself in, and the

house was filled with the deep silence of people peacefully sleeping. Quietly, she crept upstairs.

The first thing she saw in her room was the diary, lying on the floor where she'd dropped it when Joe had phoned. It struck her as prophetic that it had fallen open at an entry dated in the spring of her sixteenth year.

May 20

Dear Diary, Went to the long weekend beef barbecue at the beach with Rick Aldren this afternoon. Joe D. showed up on his Harley, with his date hanging on behind. He was wearing denim cutoffs and a shirt open practically to the waist so that the hair on his chest showed. He's gorgeous. And so sexy. Wonder what it would be like to have him for a boyfriend but I guess I'll never find out.

And you never did, Imogen thought, slapping the diary closed. *But you found out only too well what it felt like to have him dump you once he'd had his way with you, so if you must keep dipping into the past, at least have the good sense to learn from it, and don't make the same mistake again.*

CHAPTER FIVE

AFTER leaving her, Joe rode through the countryside for hours, skirting the small towns and sticking to the narrow, winding side roads, with nothing but the waning moon for company. Some time between three and four in the morning, he pulled over and walked for a spell beside a creek. Usually, a spin on the bike cleared his head, but not tonight. Tonight there was no escaping the thoughts swirling through his mind. He was going to have to wrestle them into order.

Ahead, an outcropping of flat rock overhung the water. Making his way to the end, he sat down, planted his feet apart, rested his elbows on his bent knees and stared moodily into space.

He wasn't normally a man given to retrospection. The way he saw it, what was done was done. He liked to think he'd learned a few things over the years—to respect courage, to value loyalty, to despise cruelty. And to live with the knowledge that he'd killed a man, albeit accidentally.

To learn some eight years after the fact that he had another's blood on his hands—his own child's, God help him!—almost destroyed him. Not because he was arrogant enough to think he could have altered the outcome of the birth, but because he could and should have prevented the conception. He couldn't shift responsibility elsewhere. The blame sat squarely on him.

"Do you remember?" Imogen had asked.

Hell, yes, he remembered! All too well.

* * *

Smuggling booze into the prom was as much a part of
the hoopla surrounding the event as the fact that a few
of the grads—guys, as a rule—ended the evening with
their heads down the nearest toilet and nothing but the
mother of all hangovers the next morning to remind
them they were supposed to have had a blast the night
before.

Nothing had changed from the time Joe had graduated, five years earlier, which was why he offered to be
there when the bash ended, to make sure his sister got
home safely.

The dance had been held at the Briarwood. He left his
Harley at the end of the parking lot near the hotel gardens, figuring he had time for a cigarette before Patsy
showed up. He'd been a fool in more ways than one
back then. Smoking, speeding, womanizing. But that
night had changed everything. He'd never been the same
since.

At first he hadn't paid attention to the muttered
exchange taking place on the other side of the tree he
was leaning against. Had, in fact, been on the verge of
distancing himself from the sound of heavy breathing
punctuated by the rustle of clothing being shoved aside.
He saw enough action of his own, and got no thrill from
listening in on some other guy putting the moves on a
girl.

But then he realized something wasn't right. If the
hysterical edge in the girl's voice as she begged, "Don't,
please…please, stop it!" hadn't been enough to alert
him, the sound of fabric tearing, followed by muffled
tears, had.

Tossing the cigarette aside, he plowed through the
fancy shrubbery, no doubt leaving a trail of destruction
in his wake, and come upon Philip Maitland, son of the

mayor, slobbering drunkenly all over the Palmer princess. There was enough of a moon for Joe to see the dress hanging off her shoulder, the half-bared breast, the glimpse of thigh exposed by Maitland's obscene groping. And the tears pouring down her face as she struggled to get away.

Given all that, he'd hardly been left with a choice. Hurling himself forward, he grabbed Maitland in a full nelson, spun him around and, for good measure, gave him a boot in the butt that sent him sprawling face first in a flower bed. The last time he bothered to look, the mayor's son had been bent double, retching over a bed of petunias.

The girl hadn't been in much better shape. It was less her pitiful attempts to cover herself than the look of blank terror on her face that had moved him to go to her, haul her upright and wrap his arms around her.

She quivered in his hold, her breathing, as rapid and shallow as if she'd run a three-minute mile, fluttering against his throat. And her eyes—wide open, unblinking, unfocused—had stared through him to a horror only she could see.

"Here," he said, shucking off his jacket and trying to drape it around her shoulders without touching her. A guy didn't need a degree in psychology to see that her panic was merely in a holding pattern, waiting to attack again at the slightest provocation. And he wasn't at all sure she knew he was there to help her, not hurt her.

She stood passively, helpless as a kitten caught in a storm.

"Is there someone you'd like me to call?" he asked. "Your mother, perhaps, or a taxi?"

She jerked to life then, rearing away from him as if he'd threatened to run a picture of her, all torn and di-

sheveled, on the front page of the *Daily Herald*. "No!"
she exclaimed in a shocked whisper. "No one must see
me like this! Please, *please,* couldn't *you* take me
home?"

There wasn't room for two to ride pillion on the bike,
and Patsy, who had an eleven-thirty curfew, would be
looking for him any minute. But he could hardly walk
away from the princess. "Sure," he said. "Just wait here
while I take care of a couple of things." Then, seeing
the terrified way she glanced at Maitland groveling in
the dirt, added, "Don't worry, he's one of the things I'm
taking care of. He won't be bothering you again tonight."

"Thank you," she whimpered. He guessed that being
polite, even in the face of disaster, came as naturally to
her as cursing did to him.

He yanked Maitland to his feet and frog-marched him
through the gardens to an ornamental pond where carp
swam. "Sorry about the company, kids," he told the
fish, and pitched Maitland headfirst into the drink before
going inside the hotel to find a phone and arrange for
Sean to come and pick up Patsy.

Five minutes later, he was at the spot where Imogen
waited. By then, reaction had set in and her teeth were
rattling as if she'd been left out all night in a winter
storm. "Hey," he said softly, "it's over. Everything's
okay now."

But they were empty words, and he knew it. She'd
been violated, and he wasn't sure she'd ever be over it.
"How could I have been so stupid?" she whispered bro-
kenly.

He'd wondered that himself. He was damn sure Patsy
knew better than to wander off in the dark with a drunk.
"Couldn't you tell he was three sheets to the wind?"

"No! How could he be? There was no alcohol served at the dance. We're all underage."

The shock with which she made that remark had shown the extent of her innocence, which made his own behavior all the more unforgivable. If he'd had any idea how the evening would end, he'd have walked away from her and let someone else play knight-errant.

Even in those days, though, he had a knack for leaping into a situation without weighing the risks and possible consequences. So he hoisted her on the back of the Harley, handed her the spare helmet and drove her to her fancy mansion at the top of Clifton Hill.

The memory of that ride burned particularly bright. Hardly surprising, given that they'd shared a similar ride only a few hours ago, the only difference being that now she'd blossomed into a woman whose curves were more lushly defined than those of the girl he'd ridden away with then. Still, he could recall in vivid detail how he felt, speeding through the night with the rushing air flattening his T-shirt to his chest, her arms clutched around his waist, the warmth of her body at his back. Like a hero. Except heroes didn't take advantage of a woman in distress, no matter what the circumstances.

They were almost at the gates to her house when he realized she was trying to tell him something. Pulling to the side of the road, he turned his head toward her. "Sorry, I didn't catch what you said."

Her face was a pale blur at his shoulder, her voice as light as a moth's wing fluttering at his ear. "I don't want anyone to see how I... Could we go in by the back entrance, do you think? It's only a mile or two down the road."

"Whatever you say, my lady."

He should have known he was on dangerous ground

when he started talking like some eighteenth-century poet wasting away with brain rot. If he'd had a grain of sense, he'd have told her only someone with reason to feel guilty needed to sneak in the back door, and from everything he'd seen, she'd been blameless in the night's events.

He hadn't had a grain of sense. Instead, he'd done as she asked and marveled that what she called the back entrance was grander by far than anything to be found in his section of town. Slowly, he drove past a gate-keeper's lodge and cruised along a path just wide enough to take a small truck. Eventually, they arrived at a trio of greenhouses.

"I can walk from here," she said, slipping from the bike.

A belt of trees separated the working end of the estate from the formal gardens. Apart from the faint sheen of moonlight reflected by the glass of the greenhouses, it had been too dark to see more than a couple of feet.

Turning off the ignition and leaning the bike on its kickstand, he said, "I'll come with you."

"No," she said. "I've put you to enough trouble already."

"Sorry, princess," he said, taking her firmly by the arm, "but I don't do things by half. I've brought you this far. I'll see to it you make it safely the rest of the way."

Jeez, what a sanctimonious jerk he'd been, and for what? To prove within the hour that he was no better than Maitland, out to gratify his own needs with little regard for hers?

They followed a trail through the trees and eventually came to the clearing where the cottage stood. "What is this place?" he asked, beginning to think he'd stumbled into some sort of fairy tale. The only thing missing was a trail of bread crumbs and some ancient hag cackling at the door.

"My old playhouse."

"Some playhouse!"

"It's only one room," she said, as if that made any difference. Hell, he could name a couple of families in Lister's Meadows who'd have thought the place a palace.

His jacket hung on her narrow frame. Pushing back one sleeve, she clutched the collar close to her throat. "I can't let my mother see me like this, so I'll wait here until I know she's in bed before I go to the house."

Years must have gone by since the place had been used. The door was jammed, its wood warped from too much winter frost and summer humidity. When she finally realized it wasn't going to open for her, she sagged against the frame and began to cry. He realized then she wasn't nearly as much in command of the situation as she thought she was.

"Here," he said, pushing her gently aside, "let me."

Putting his shoulder to it, he rammed the door open with one shove and ended up half-stumbling across the threshold. Inside, it was dark as a cave. "Watch your step," he warned her, swiping at the cobwebs sticking to his face.

He heard her footsteps approach and felt rather than saw her standing beside him. The next thing he knew, she'd slipped her hand into his. "You don't suppose there are mice in here, do you?" she asked fearfully.

"No," he lied, knowing damned well all manner of wildlife had likely made a home there over the years. "Is the place hooked up with electricity, by any chance?"

"No. When I was little, I only ever came during the day in the summer."

"Check my jacket. There's a cigarette lighter in one of the pockets."

She fumbled a moment, then her voice came again, a little less rattled than before. "Here it is."

He reached for it, ignoring the sweet brush of her fingers against his, and flicking it open, he adjusted the flame as high as it would go. Shadows jumped crazily over the low ceiling and around the room, but there was enough light to see the hand-me-down Oriental rug covering the wooden floorboards. A child's rocking chair sat under one window with a toy cradle next to it. Beside the other window was a table where a little girl might have entertained her dolls to tea. Patsy at eight or nine would have gone ballistic if she'd seen the place.

But as an adult refuge? "You can't stay here, princess," he said scornfully as she slipped off his jacket and tried to return it to him. "Let me take you home. If it'll help any, I'll explain to your mother what happened tonight. She can't hold you responsible."

"Oh, I couldn't possibly!" Her eyes had grown huge, each pupil reflecting the lighter flame in perfect miniature. "You don't understand. I can't let my mother see…all this."

She looked at the ragged, grass-stained dress, at her white satin shoes, which were in even sadder shape. And, God help him, he looked at her.

His glance had gone from the crushed fabric to her hair, all pale, shimmering gold in the flickering light. From her hands, trembling as she tried to put herself to rights, to her neck, rising smooth as cream above the torn bodice of her gown.

She cringed before his scrutiny. "I feel so dirty," she

whispered, a fresh crop of tears sparkling suddenly on the tips of her lashes. "So cheap and stupid."

He'd known about sex, about allure, about all kinds of things that draw a man to a woman. But until that night and that moment with Imogen, he had not known about pure, feminine grace, and he had no concept at all of fragility. Only when he looked into her eyes and saw her bruised spirit staring at him had he begun to understand, and by then it was too late for either of them.

He reached out to her, his aim solely to reassure her, to try to heal her. Without a second's hesitation, she came to him. Snapping off the lighter, he pulled her into his arms. "You're none of those things, princess," he muttered, burying her face against his neck and stroking the supple, trembling length of her spine.

The fragrance of her skin, her hair, rose to captivate him. She smelled of loveliness and everything a woman ought to be. He knew no other way to describe it. Of spring-filled days and hot summer nights, of passion and innocence. Unforgettable. Intoxicating.

Without warning, his blood had surged, leaving him tight and aching. At the back of his mind, a voice had warned him to put a stop to things before they went too far. But his mind wasn't in charge anymore.

Nor, it appeared, was hers. She softened in his arms. The trembling stopped. She turned her face toward him and without premeditation he found himself kissing her. She kissed him back, her mouth warm and soft and willing.

There was no disguising his arousal. Nor had she seemed offended by it, if the way she tilted against him was any indication. He wasn't conscious of sliding his hand down to cup her hip and press her closer and couldn't, if his life had depended on it, have said when they began moving together in a slow, sinuous prologue to intimacy.

One thing led to another, that was all. There in that dumb little house, on that threadbare old rug, with nothing but a brief flood of moonlight to gild the moment, he made love to her with more tenderness and care than he'd thought himself capable of.

She was the first virgin he'd had. Tight and sleek, driven by nothing but instinct, too artless to pretend and too sweetly generous to withhold, she gave him all of herself. And he'd taken, losing himself inside her, the condoms he always carried lying forgotten beneath her head in the zippered inside pocket of his jacket.

Afterward, he'd been horrified. Ashamed. Disgusted with himself.

And she? She'd curled up in his arms. "Thank you, Joe!" she'd whispered, as if he'd just hung the moon for her....

If the lightening strip of sky to the east hadn't told him it was time to make a move, the predawn chill invading his limbs did. Hoisting himself to his feet, he flexed his shoulders and knees, then rotated his head to ease the stiffness in his neck.

His eyes felt gritty from lack of sleep, and he was so hungry his stomach was folding in on itself. Not the best shape for a man to be in when he was at the controls of a powerful machine, he decided, and ambled down to splash his face in the creek.

The water was like ice, stinging him to full alertness. Shaking away the drops clinging to his hair and wiping his hands on the seat of his jeans, he headed to where he'd left the bike, at the top of a rise in the road.

By his reckoning, he'd traveled northeast out of

Rosemont after dropping off Imogen and come pretty much full circle, ending up some seventy miles west of where he'd started. Fleetingly, he entertained the idea of giving the town a wide berth and riding on, not stopping until he was in California, in the place he'd called home for the last four years.

If he'd thought such a move would give him peace of mind, he wouldn't have hesitated. But there were too many unresolved issues nagging at his mind. For a start, why had his daughter died? Was it something that could have been prevented? Might his being there have made a difference, as Imogen had more or less implied?

If so, that mother of hers had plenty to answer for, because contrary to what Imogen seemed to believe, he *had* attempted to keep in touch. Had, in fact, presented himself at the front door a couple of days later and been told in no uncertain terms to take a hike because the daughter of the house was so determined to sever any connection that she had fled town rather than run the risk of having to see him again.

No, he wasn't going anywhere until he got some answers.

Wheeling the bike into the middle of the road, he sat for a moment, looking at the valley below. A farm nestled in a hollow, with a windbreak of trees around it. Already lights showed at the windows and a thin column of smoke rose from the chimney to hang motionless in the air. He heard the faint clang of metal on metal coming from an outbuilding, the stamping of hooves on cement, and knew a sudden sense of loss for what might have been.

He could have been happy with such a life if circumstances had been different. A spread of land to call his own, horses in the stables, a wife, a child. If only Imogen had come to him and their baby had lived...

Impatiently, he inhaled a lungful of the fresh, sharp air and slipped the bike into gear. With any luck, he'd be back in time to sit down to breakfast in his mother's kitchen—ham, eggs, hash-brown potatoes and gallons of coffee to keep him on his toes. He was going to need all the fortification he could get for what he intended to accomplish that day.

Surprisingly, Suzanne decided to attend the retirement ceremony with Imogen. "Well, why not?" she asked, apparently quite recovered from her migraine of the night before. "Apart from the fact that I received an invitation—as indeed I should have, given that I served eight years on the school board—I rather like the idea of going out with my daughter. When, after all, was the last time you and I were seen in public together, Imogen?"

Imogen didn't point out that it had been the day her mother had driven her away from the clinic in Ferndale and dropped her off at the nearest airport. Why spoil the occasion with dark reminders when it was obvious that Suzanne was trying to do her part to mend matters between them?

The auditorium was filling fast. Imogen recognized quite a few faces in passing, but Joe's was not among them. It was just as well. After last night, she wasn't sure she could look him in the eye with any degree of composure. That kiss they'd shared had wreaked too much havoc.

Slipping into a seat next to the center aisle, she looked around, thinking that the place didn't look so very different from the last time she'd been there, the day she

received her high school diploma. Now, as then, a great
bank of flowers decorated the stage. The same polished
lectern sat center front, with a row of chairs fanning out
on either side.

She'd been one of twenty-three graduates, as full of
dreams as the rest and just as sure that life after school
held nothing but success and good fortune. How quickly
it all had changed for her! Less than twenty-four hours
later, her future lay in ruins.

The lights in the auditorium flickered, then dimmed,
a warning that the ceremony was about to begin. A hush
stole over the assembly. The school music teacher raised
his baton and led the band into the school song as the
platform party, composed of the usual dignitaries, filed
on stage.

"When we convened to discuss how best to honor
you, Miss Duncliffe," the emcee said, once he got past
his preliminary welcome, "we decided that the most
meaningful accolades would surely be those offered by
people who, like me, were once your students. You
might not remember all the names or faces of the people
you'll be seeing in the next little while, but they have
never forgotten you. And so, without further ado, let me
introduce our first guest."

Imogen settled back in her seat, prepared to enjoy herself and feeling more relaxed in her mother's company
than she'd have thought possible a week ago. The trib-
utes ranged from touching to entertaining, reducing even
Suzanne to ladylike titters on occasion. But when the
last guest was announced and Joe walked on stage,
Imogen was struck with the treacherous sense of having
the ground dissolve beneath her feet.

The sight of him all spruced up in a navy suit, white
shirt and burgundy tie took her breath away. Unable to

help herself, she drank in the sight of him, the lean elegance of his hands casually gripping the lectern, his eyes ranging the audience and seeming to come to rest on her with such intimacy that she thought her lungs would seize up.

He began to speak, amusingly, it seemed, since everyone around her was laughing, but she, too mesmerized by the movement of his lips as they shaped words, heard nothing. Instead, she found herself so thoroughly caught up in reliving last night's kiss that her mouth stung from the memory of it.

In his present mood, Joe Donnelly was hard to resist. His charm was almost palpable, his easy assurance far removed from the bad-boy image he'd once taken such pains to promote.

After he concluded his remarks, the superintendent of schools presented Miss Duncliffe with her retirement gift, and the ceremony drew to a close with a reminder of the strawberry tea to follow on the playing field.

Suzanne, her mood unaccountably altered, sniffed disapprovingly. "I think we'll give that a miss," she declared, as they emerged from the auditorium into the brilliant heat of the afternoon. "We'll be far more comfortable at Deepdene, and I do so dislike crowds."

But Imogen hadn't come all the way to Rosemont to fall into the same old bad habit of letting her mother dictate her every move. "If that's what you'd prefer, then by all means go, Mother, but I plan to stay and catch up with friends I haven't seen in years."

Her mother met the suggestion with amused disdain. "Oh, Imogen, I hardly think—" But the familiar air of disapproval had lost its power to influence, and Suzanne knew it. "I hardly think," she amended, "that I should leave, then. We ought to present a united front."

The tea tent was busy, but they managed to find a table at one end. And then, suddenly, Joe materialized from the crowd and stood directly in front of them. "I was hoping I'd track you down in here. How are you, Mrs. Palmer?"

His smile, candid and warm enough to melt stone, failed to move Suzanne. "Do I know you?" she inquired, fixing him in a stare designed to freeze him into extinction.

Joe wasn't fazed in the slightest. "We have met, Mrs. Palmer, but it was a long time ago. I'm Joe Donnelly. From Lister's Meadows."

He flung the words down like a challenge, and despite the heat of the afternoon, a chill feathered the back of Imogen's neck. Joe was up to no good. She knew it as well she knew her own name. And Suzanne looked as if she was going to have a stroke.

"I was hoping," he went on, with the watchful delight of a particularly smug tomcat waiting to pounce on a mouse, "that we could have tea together. It's been so long since we visited."

"I don't know what you're talking about, young man," Suzanne retorted, her tone as glacial as her features, "nor do I care to stay and find out. And may I say I find your accosting me in this fashion nothing short of impertinent."

She stood and attempted to leave. But Joe was not about to be so easily dismissed. "It has never been my intention to offend you, ma'am. I merely thought we might—"

"I'm afraid not."

"Okay." He shrugged and turned his attention to Imogen. His glance swept over her patent leather pumps, the gold fob watch at the lapel of her ivory blazer, the diamonds in her ears and, finally rested with potent dedication on her mouth.

Almost dissolving in the heat of his scrutiny, she took refuge beneath the brim of her straw boater, at which he bent and touched a finger to her chin. "You're looking even lovelier today than you did last night, Imogen," he said.

"Last night?" Suzanne echoed faintly, sinking into her seat.

Still holding Imogen's gaze, he said, "Didn't she tell you, Mrs. Palmer? We spent quite a bit of time together yesterday, catching up on old times."

A hint of panic colored her mother's voice. "Imogen? Is this true?"

"Yes," Imogen said, completely enthralled by him.

He'd visited the barber, and for today, at least, the blue jeans had been abandoned in favor of his well-cut suit, but underneath he was still a maverick. It would take more than a knife-edged crease in his pants and a conservative haircut to reduce a man like Joe Donnelly to the ranks of the ordinary.

Other people recognized it, too. Given that he stood well over six feet tall, with a physique that tapered from shoulder to hip with stupendous muscular grace, it was hardly surprising. But it was not just his stature or that face, with its heavily lashed, startlingly blue eyes, chiseled jaw or sudden, devastating smile that earned him a second glance. It was the aura of lawlessness that no amount of surface respectability could erase.

Watching him, Imogen was reminded of the time she'd first become aware of him as someone other than Patsy's big brother who sometimes helped out in his father's garage. She'd been about sixteen and had left school a few minutes early for a dental appointment.

He'd been in the parking lot behind the auditorium, waiting as he often did to take Patsy to the hospital, where she worked as a junior volunteer two afternoons a week. Clad in the black leather jacket and boots that had been his uniform in those days, his dark hair curling over his collar and his helmet dangling from one hand, he'd been a sight to strike an uneasy thrill in a girl of Imogen's sheltered upbringing.

Then, as now, he'd given her a thorough once-over, his gaze traveling from her feet to her face and back in insolent appraisal. She had stared, fascinated. His body language, the angle of shoulder and hips, the way he'd straddled his motorcycle, had spelled pure animal magnetism. Her reaction—a strange, electric ripple in the pit of her stomach—had almost paralyzed her.

As if he'd known exactly the effect he was having on her, he smiled, a slow, provocative smile. Eventually he spoke, his voice rolling over her like sin, dark and delicious and forbidden. "Something I can do for you, honey?"

She'd almost drowned in the fiery blush that had swept over her. No one had ever called her *honey* before. Endearments were not common in her family.

Heat had surged through every pore in her body and left her gasping for air—and deliverance. "I'm going to the dentist," she squeaked irrelevantly. "I don't want to be late."

"Want a lift?" he asked, at which she'd just about had a heart attack. If he'd said, "Want to neck?", she couldn't have been more horrified—or thrilled!

He bathed her in the same smile now, as if they shared some private joke too delicious to share with the rest of the world, and injected the same wickedly conspiratorial tone in his voice. "We sort of left things hanging last night, didn't we?"

"Yes," she breathed, no more in command of herself than she'd been at sixteen.

"I'd like to pick up where we left off. Will you have dinner with me tonight?" He tugged his lapels and shrugged disarmingly. "It's not often I get dressed up, and I hate to let the occasion go to waste."

Ignoring Suzannne's whimper of distress, Imogen said yes again, aware that a kind of meltdown was occurring inside her and not caring a bit. If he'd suggested flying to the moon, she'd have said yes to that, too. Not to show her mother that she was permanently out from under her thumb but because the Joe Donnelly of today was as woefully irresistible as he'd been before he'd acquired the polish and urbanity of a mature man.

He had kissed her and it had been nothing short of wonderful. It did no good to remind herself she'd been burned enough to know better than to play with fire. The simple fact was she yearned for him more intensely than ever, if truth be told. And what, after all, was so very wrong with that?

They had both grown up in the interim. They didn't have to repeat old mistakes. They could explore the possibility of a relationship founded on trust and friendship and mutual attraction, couldn't they, and see where that led them?

Friendship, Imogen? She blushed at the mendacity of such rationalizing. *Oh, I think you've got a lot more in mind than that!*

He shot back his cuff to check his watch. "Are you free to leave now? I have in mind a place on the river out Peterborough way, but it'll take us a couple of hours to get there."

She looked at her slim-fitting skirt. "Not on the motorcycle, I hope?"

"No." He laughed, making further inroads on her susceptibility, and extended his elbow in courtly invitation. "This time we travel in style, princess."

So what if she had more in mind than friendship? If she believed in herself and him, shouldn't she reach out and hold on to the possibility with all her strength?

Squaring her shoulders, she tucked her hand more firmly in the crook of his arm and cast him a deliberately flirtatious look from beneath her lashes. "Then let's stop wasting time and go," she said.

CHAPTER SIX

HE HALF expected her mother to come chasing after them, screeching protests and forcibly restraining Imogen from leaving with him. But they reached the car without incident and joined the slow line of vehicles crawling toward the single exit from the parking lot.

They didn't talk much on the way to the restaurant. He'd borrowed Sean's prized 1955 Thunderbird and was happy to concentrate on seeing what it could do on the open road. Imogen tossed her hat behind her seat and seemed equally content to enjoy the ride with only an occasional comment on the passing scenery. He was glad. For some reason, he suddenly felt as uptight and tongue-tied as a kid on his first date.

He couldn't figure out why. Because it wasn't a date, nor had he asked her out on impulse. There was unfinished business between them, that was all, and it had seemed best to complete it where they weren't likely to run into people they knew. In light of the number of people roaming the streets this week, there was slim chance of that happening in Rosemont. Yet given his inability to keep his hands off her when they were alone, it had seemed prudent to choose a reasonably public place where he'd have no choice but to restrain his baser urges.

They arrived at the restaurant shortly before seven and were shown to a table at the rear of the building, on a screened porch overlooking a garden. ''What a lovely old place,'' she said, after they'd decided on their meal and the wine he ordered had been poured. "How did you find out about it?"

"Read about it in a magazine at my mom's," he told her. "It was originally a mill, built in the early eighteen hundreds."

Their first course arrived, with the waiter making a big production of grinding pepper all over everything.

"So," he said, once they were alone again, "how did you like this afternoon's shindig?"

"I thought it was wonderful. Entertaining and very moving." She laughed and leaned back in a slither of hidden silk. Instead of a blouse beneath her jacket, she had on only a satin and lace camisole that shifted around in a way that had a man's brain lagging far behind other parts of his anatomy. "I particularly enjoyed your contribution to the program."

"Thanks." Squirming, he repositioned his linen napkin on his lap and wished they'd ordered saltpeter as an appetizer instead of oysters on the half shell. "And this place—is it okay, or would you have preferred something less rustic?"

"No! Joe, it's charming here." She looked at the old timbers and simple whitewashed walls, then at the garden below where a blaze of marigolds ran amok in the long grass under a gnarled old apple tree. "Even the flowers are lovely, don't you think?"

"I guess," he said, finding her a lot more distracting than a half-wild garden. "Why aren't you eating your salad? Is there something wrong with it?"

"It's fine." But her actions belied the words. In fact, she pushed her plate aside and, turning her attention to her wineglass, ran a fingertip around its rim then suddenly blurted out, "Actually, something's bothering me, and I've been wanting to bring it up since we left the school, but I was afraid of spoiling the evening by mentioning it. But it'll be spoiled, anyway, if I don't get this off my chest, so please let me say how embarrassed I am at the way my mother treated you this afternoon. I don't know why she was so rude.''

''I do,'' he said, laying down his fork. ''She's afraid of me.''

She stared at him in disbelief. ''That's ridiculous!''

He paused, debating the wisdom of telling her about his unforgettable meeting with Suzanne Palmer nine years before. He decided against it. Not only did he not want it to seem he'd used the woman's behavior as an excuse for his shabby defection, he didn't want to be the cause of another rift between mother and daughter.

Not that he wouldn't have liked to blow the old biddy's cover wide open, just as he was sure she'd have done, if the situation were reversed. But this wasn't about her, it was about Imogen and him. So he said, ''It's not ridiculous, princess. She knows I'm the one who got you pregnant and she doesn't want you getting mixed-up with me again. And I can't say I blame her. I wouldn't want to see my daughter get hurt if I could possibly do anything to prevent it.''

''Is that what's going to happen, Joe? Are you planning to hurt me?''

''Not if I can help it. But that's no guarantee it won't happen anyway.''

''It's a chance I'm prepared to take,'' she said. ''I wouldn't be here now if I weren't.''

''I hurt you before, badly.''

''Yes,'' she said.

He finished his oysters and flicked a glance out the window before focusing on her again. ''One of the reasons I asked you out tonight, Imogen, was to tell you how much I wish I could change what happened that night—or at least change the outcome.''

''Are you saying you regret the part you played?''

''I regret everything. You should never have been subjected to Maitland's behavior, and I should never have taken advantage of the state you were in because of him.''

''You saved my sanity that night, Joe. Don't you know that?''

''And put you through hell afterward. I've been haunted by what you implied last night—that I was to blame for the baby's death.''

Her eyes darkened in dismay. ''Oh, please!'' she said, touching her left hand to her heart—or more accurately, her breast. An innocent gesture, it nevertheless drew his attention to the creamy hint of cleavage beneath her camisole. ''I was wrong. I had—''

He cleared his throat and dragged his mind to where it belonged. ''No, you were right. Because it was my fault you got pregnant. That's one thing I could and should have prevented. And I didn't because I got too caught up in the moment.'' He blew out a rueful breath. ''You were a damsel in real distress, and I got carried away with the idea of playing knight to the rescue.''

''And what was wrong with that?'' she asked softly. ''I think you should be proud.''

''I didn't protect you. I made things worse.''

''Would you feel better if I told you that I've never once regretted what we did?'' She spread her pretty hands on the table and examined them, as if she didn't dare look him in the eye while she made her next confession. ''You were the most exciting man I'd ever met, and I fell in love with you that night.''

''That wasn't love.'' He felt obliged to point it out.

"You might have thought it was at the time because doing so made it easier for you to face the consequences of what followed. But you weren't to blame for anything that happened that night. You were just a kid, too young by far to be associating with a guy like me."

"I was eighteen, Joe. Old enough to say no if I'd wanted to. But I didn't. I couldn't. Of course, I knew I wasn't like the girls you usually went with. I was too naive, too unsophisticated to hold your interest for very long. But still I hoped that what we shared meant something special to you, too, and that I'd see you again. I admit that when I realized I was pregnant and you'd left town, I was afraid and very unhappy. But even when things were at their worst, I could never bring myself to regret that it was your baby I was carrying."

She skewered him through the heart with that. "I wish I'd known about the baby, Imogen," he said, his voice thick with sudden emotion. "I wish things had turned out the way you wanted."

"Well, they didn't, yet I've managed to move forward and make something of my life." She waited until their plates were cleared and the main course served, then shot him a sudden mischievous smile. "Shall I tell you what I wish? That we'd just met for the first time this week, as equals. Because one thing hasn't changed. You're still the most exciting man I've ever known."

"And we still come from different worlds, princess," he said quickly, before her admission could seduce him into believing otherwise.

"I said as equals, Joe, and I meant it. Because as far as I'm concerned, that's what we are and always have been."

He looked at her—at the way she wore her clothes, at her natural grace and elegance—and knew he should put a stop to her delusions before things got seriously out of hand. The plain fact was that he could dress up in the best a European tailor had to offer, but at heart, he was a blue jeans kind of guy. For him to entertain, even briefly, the idea that they'd ever make a couple was asking for nothing but trouble he didn't need.

Four years ago, he'd sailed away from Ojo del Diablo a free man, and it had taken a lot of hard work since to get to where he was today. He'd be a fool to shoot himself in the foot now.

So why did he risk looking past the outward trimmings and into her soul where the girl he'd once found irresistible still lurked, as defenseless now as she'd been then? Why did the discovery create such confusion in him, making it impossible for him to adhere to his code of survival?

If she'd become super gorgeous or sexily coy, as so many women with her background and money did, he could have ignored what she said. But her quiet glamour, the prettiness that came of being a blue-eyed, natural blonde who didn't need to rely on makeup and, most of all, her honesty and vulnerability, had him wanting to touch her, to take what she offered. And to say... Damn it all, to say things far better left unsaid.

Suddenly furious with her for uncovering a weakness in himself he found both humiliating and intolerable, he said curtly, "I no more believe that than you do, Imogen, so let's cut the flattery and get down to business."

"Business?"

"That's right. You only covered part of the story last night. Tell me the rest about my daughter."

"The rest?" She no more understood the anger in his tone than he did, and stared at him wide-eyed with hurt and bewilderment. "But I've told you everything, Joe. What else is there to say?"

"You can tell me how much she weighed, why she died, what you called her." Hardening his heart against her whimper of distress, he plunged on, despising the way he was behaving but driven by a deep-seated need to know, to understand. "And most important, where she's buried. I want to visit her grave, Imogen. I want her to know her father cares that she was born."

She seemed to shrink. "I can't tell you those things," she said, in a small, defeated voice.

"Yes, you can. You owe me that much."

"I can't," she repeated, shaking her head, "because I don't know myself."

"Don't hand me that!" he said scornfully. "Of course you know. She was a full-term baby. Her birth and death are a matter of record."

"But I was never told the details."

"Why not?"

"It was a difficult labor. At the end, they gave me an anesthetic. When I woke up, I'd been moved from the delivery suite to a private room on a different floor, and it was all over. My mother was sitting by my bed. She broke the news to me and said she'd taken care of everything."

He gave an exclamation of disgust. "And you just let it go at that? You didn't even ask to see our child? You let them ship her off to some morgue without once holding her in your arms?"

Her chin quivered and tears hung in her eyes, but she refused to let them fall. She tilted her patrician little nose, looked him squarely in the eye and said, "Yes. For once, I was happy to let my mother take charge. And since you're so anxious to learn all the facts, I'll

CATHERINE SPENCER   95

tell you why. Because at the time, I didn't care. All I wanted was to be dead, too. I felt I had nothing to live for. *Nothing!* For months after, I went through the motions of living and kept my grief bottled up inside.''

"A person doesn't find closure that way. Why else do you think people put themselves through the agony of funerals? Because they need to say goodbye. And you'd have been a sight better off if you'd followed that route.''

"Of course I would have," she whispered. "But I didn't. Instead, I ran away. For a whole year, I traveled through North Africa, India, Malaysia, working in places where people have so little that anything you can do to make their lives easier is a gift beyond price.''

"You *worked?*"

She lifted her chin defiantly. "Yes, I did! It helped to keep my mind off my own troubles. But a person can run only so far before reality catches up. It wasn't until I was in Thailand that the reality of my child's death finally caught up with me, and by then it was too late.''

"It's never too late, Imogen," he said, his anger subsiding into shame when he saw how his bullying had wounded her. He reached out to grasp her hands where they lay on the table. They felt cold as ice. Folding them in the warmth of his, he said, "Somewhere there's a grave. I think, if you're ever to know real peace of mind, you need to find that place. I know I do.''

She started crying, a silent outpouring of tears that rolled down her cheeks and onto her jacket. She sat perfectly straight, so still she might have been cast in marble. Nothing moved except those great, quiet, endless tears.

And to his horror and embarrassment, he felt his eyes fill. She wasn't the only one who'd tried to avoid facing up to reality. Ever since he'd learned about the baby, he'd tamped down his own pain, refusing to let it gain the upper hand, determined to outrun it. But suddenly it burst free inside him with such force that the only way he could contain it was to clamp his jaw so tightly his teeth hurt.

How long it took him to gain control he didn't know. Too long, certainly, because suddenly she uttered a quietly desperate plea. "My hands!" she said, and he realized he was crushing her fingers in his.

"Sorry," he muttered, releasing them, and dared to look at her. "Why don't we get the hell out of here?"

She nodded and went to the ladies' room while he took care of the bill. "Was the meal not to your satisfaction, sir?" the waiter asked, worried.

"It was fine," he said, leaving a generous tip. "We just weren't as hungry as we thought."

He waited outside for her. It was that time of day between sunset and dark. The air was filled with the smell of growing things, flowers and grass and new leaves on the trees. They'd already rolled up the sidewalks in town, and the only sound in the still air was the quiet burble of the river running beside the mill.

Did his daughter lie in some spot as peaceful? Were there flowers growing on her grave, or did it lie neglected and choked with weeds—as choked as he suddenly found himself, so painfully that he could hardly breathe?

He was leaning on the parapet of the little humpbacked bridge, watching the waterwheel's slow turning, when she came out of the restaurant.

"Why don't we walk a bit?" he asked, when she

joined him. "There's a path beside the river, and it's still early. Or do you have to get back home?"

"No, Joe," she said mockingly. "I can come and go as I please. And I'd like to walk."

He took her arm and steered her down a rickety flight of brick-lined steps to where low-wattage lamps strung on an overhead wire marked the path. "You mentioned being in Thailand," he said. "What was it about the country that had such an effect on you?"

"I worked in an orphanage near the Laotian border. There were so many children, some so sick they were just waiting to die. It broke my heart to see them, especially the babies. There was one in particular, a little girl four months old, but she was so tiny she might have been a newborn. Maybe that was what made her so special to me. I loved taking care of her, loved the way she'd burrow into my neck when I held her."

She swallowed, once again fighting tears. "One day, she began to run a fever. By evening, she had trouble breathing. There was an old rattan rocking chair in the nursery. I sat there with her the whole night, watching her sleep and listening to the wheezing of her poor, congested little lungs."

He heard the break in her voice and took her hand. It didn't matter that he said not a word. His touch was comfort enough, and gave her the strength to finish what she'd started.

"Some time after midnight, I fell asleep. When I woke up, she was dead in my arms." She stopped, dazed at the depth of her pain. She had not expected to find it easy to tell him, but neither had she known it would this hard. "You might find it difficult to believe, Joe, but I think that was when I finally faced up to our baby's death. I mourned that little orphan as if she'd been my own. Even now, it's her face I see whenever I think about our daughter. Not long after that, I came back to Canada and took up work that had nothing to do with children so I wouldn't be faced every day with reminders of what I'd lost.''

"Damn your mother!" he said, with sudden vehemence. "And damn everyone in that hospital who conspired with her to shut you out of—''

"It wasn't their fault," she said. "They meant well. And I went along with them.''

"And because of them, you still haven't put your baby to rest, Imogen," he said, his voice a murmur. "You need to do that.''

Perhaps he was right, but she was afraid of the poignant memories such action might stir up, afraid she might fall back into the dark pit of despair that had been the legacy of her night of love with him. But she didn't expect him to understand that. He'd never been afraid of anything in his life.

"I don't know that I can," she said, bracing herself for another outburst of scorn from him.

Stopping under the canopy of a willow tree, he tugged her so she was facing him and standing so close that his words winnowed over her face. "Yes, you can, princess," he said, running his hands up her arms and over her shoulders. "Because we'll go together. This is one thing you won't have to do alone.''

Then, as he had the night before, he leaned forward and kissed her, a long, slow kiss full of tenderness. It seemed the most natural thing in the world to sink into that kiss, to drown in it. To let her breasts cushion the unyielding plane of his chest, her hips nest against his. And when his mouth grew subtly more assertive, to let her lips open in soft welcome.

Briefly, he raised his head and stared solemnly at her, the question in his eyes unmistakable. *Are you sure?*

She met his gaze fearlessly. *Never more sure of anything!* Never mind that this was how things had started for them all those years ago, with a need to comfort and console. This was different. She was no longer an ingenue, stepping blindly on the path of passion without the first idea where it could lead, but a woman who knew full well the limits of her tolerance, just as she knew he was the only man on earth who could heal the aching sense of loss she'd carried for so long.

She tasted of honey and silk, of innocence and allure.

Dazed, he found himself pulling her to him and threading his fingers through her hair to weld her mouth more tightly to his. Unwilling, unable to let her go. Good God, how was it possible that the spell she'd cast on him almost a decade before had lost nothing of its power to enchant him?

The driving hunger took hold of him, goading him beyond anything a man should have to tolerate. The thoughts raced through his mind, insanely greedy, obscenely indiscreet—find a secluded place where they wouldn't be seen, here, now, bury himself in her sleek flesh, feel the shudders devour her until she convulsed around him and brought him to his own singular swift release.

His fingers slid down her throat, deftly worked apart the buttons of her jacket and found the sweet, warm valley between her breasts. She moaned and sank against him.

Frantically, he searched for a place to take her and found nothing but the forked trunk of the old willow tree. Angling himself against it, he brought her close again, burying his mouth against the thrust of her nipples beneath the silken fabric of her camisole.

He molded her hips with his palms, trailed his hands the length of her legs to the soft hollows behind her knees. At his instigation, the hem of her skirt rode high around her waist until, at last, there was nothing but the tender inner sweep of thigh beneath his hands, the secret crease of flesh.

She was damp and willing, and he was at flash point, ready to explode at a touch, so close to paradise that the exquisite torture nearly killed him.

She was the one to put an end to such madness by pulling back. Not cruelly, as he'd done the previous night, to prove himself unvanquished, but with a quiet honesty that shamed him. "It seems I don't know myself nearly as well as I thought I did," she said, her voice a breathless quiver of emotion. "I'm no more able to resist you now than I was at eighteen."

He hardly recognized the rough croak of his voice. "I doubt that."

"It's true." Unable to look him in the eye, she attempted to restore her clothing to some sort of order.

He swallowed and straightened the lapels of her jacket. "It's been an emotionally draining couple of days for both of us. People tend to overreact in such circumstances. I certainly did, last night and again tonight. And I apologize."

"Are you saying you're sorry you kissed me?"

Kissed her? He'd damn near ravished her!

The lamps lining the path threw haunting shadows over her face, emphasizing her mouth, so soft and tender it was all he could do not to lay claim to it again. And her eyes—how could he lie with that clear gaze trained on his face so artlessly?

"Yes," he said. "It wasn't a smart move."

"Why not?"

Jeez, had she always been like this, probing every word to lay bare deceit and uncovering truths she'd be better off not knowing? "Because when it comes to romantic stuff, I'm not in it for the long haul. I can't give you what you're looking for, Imogen."

"What makes you think you know what I'm looking for? You only know what I've told you about my past. You don't have the first idea what I want for the future."

"I know we're headed down different roads. We always have been. If the child we made had lived, I'd have been prepared to stand by you. But realistically, the chances of a marriage ever working out between us would have been pretty dim."

She stared at her laced fingers, then skewered him with another of those unsettling gazes. "Why?"

Aiming to lighten the moment, he said, "Because you were born with a silver spoon in your mouth, and the closest I ever came to that was the wooden spoon on my rear end when I was about eight and shaved my brother's head."

The laughter poured out of her, as pure and free as water gurgling over rocks in a creek. For a moment, she seemed to sparkle all over, and he knew another powerful urge to kiss her. Too soon, though, she sobered, and it was as if a light had gone out. "But we're not children anymore, Joe. We don't have to play by other people's rules. We can make our own."

That was when he should have put a safe distance between them, thanked her for a pleasant evening and driven her home. Instead, he cupped his hand around her jaw and said, "You don't know the risk you'd be taking,

Imogen. I've never been very good at abiding by anyone's rules, not even my own.''

''It's a chance I'm willing to take,'' she said and, turning her head, brought her mouth to rest against his hand.

Her eyes, heavy-lidded, held him transfixed. Of their own volition, his fingers uncurled and grew slack. He saw her lips part and then, with an audacity he'd never have suspected in her, she brought the tip of her tongue to play in a lazy circle in the middle of his open palm. The gesture rocked him to the soles of his feet and damn near leveled him.

''You don't know what you'd be letting yourself in for,'' he muttered again, with about as much conviction as a dying man.

''Oh, but I do. I knew what I was doing when I let you be the first man to make love to me, Joe Donnelly, so I think you can safely assume I know what I'm proposing now.''

If she had been a different kind of woman—designing, shallow, interested only in a little romantic diversion— he might have accepted her words and driven them both to the nearest motel for the night. But her guilessness saved her. Because even he wasn't cad enough to take what she seemed so willing to give without thought for what it would cost her.

''No, princess, you don't know,'' he said. ''My life isn't here in this town any more than yours is. A few days from now—a week at the most—we'll have gone our separate ways again. Are you really prepared to risk everything you've struggled to build, just to find out if what we once shared was really as good as memory's trying to tell you it was?''

''Yes. I'm tired of being cautious. It's taken meeting

you again to make me see that I've been living in a vacuum from the day they told me my baby had died, and it strikes me suddenly that if getting pregnant was a sin to begin with, wasting what's left of my life is an even greater transgression.''

If only he dared believe a brief affair would be enough to satisfy her! But she was no more the brief affair type than he was a blue blood. What she really wanted was permanence, a man to share her life with. A suitable husband. And he was about as unsuitable as pigs were for ballet dancing. Yet because they shared so much history and because he happened to be here, at this moment, with a dangerous mix of chemistry at work, she was prepared to believe he was the answer to all her dreams.

She'd never know how tempted he was to indulge her fantasy, but he had enough on his conscience without adding to its burden. So he steered her briskly along the path toward the bright lights of the parking lot and away from the beckoning, seductive shadows.

"Trying to reconstruct history isn't the way, Imogen,'' he said flatly. ''That's why I intend to find our child's grave, so I can close the door on the past, once and for all, and move on. If you're one-tenth as smart as you like to think you are, you'll do the same.''

CHAPTER SEVEN

THEY drove to Rosemont under a canopy of stars and a moon as round and silver as an old-fashioned dollar. The road unwound before them, splashed with the indigo shadows of trees in an otherwise empty and serene landscape. It was a perfect midsummer night, a lover's kind of night. The car was small, intimate. Without moving an inch in her seat, Imogen could have laid a hand on Joe's knee or rested her head on his shoulder. Yet the distance separating her from him might as well have stretched the width of an ocean, he emanated such forbidding aloofness.

And then, when she'd decided the entire journey was going to pass in silence, he spoke. Spoke? He exploded, so suddenly and unexpectedly she practically jumped out of her skin.

"You know something, princess? You shouldn't be let out without a keeper! You're all set to leap into a relationship with me based on a couple of kisses, but you'd change your mind pretty damned fast if you knew what kind of guy you'd be hooking up with."

"We go back a lot further than a couple of kisses, Joe," she retorted, rattled. "We've known each other for at least twelve years."

"Bull, Imogen! Our association can be measured in hours. We barely exchanged two words before the night I got you pregnant."

"But I *knew* you. You were part of the landscape. The few times I visited your house, you were there. I saw how protective you were of your mother and Patsy, how you helped your father at the garage. You were the best beach lifeguard for miles around and taught more kids to swim during two months of summer vacation than anyone else managed the rest of the year. I knew you were decent and kind.''

"Oh, Christopher Columbus!'' he scoffed. "You'll be nominating me for sainthood next!''

"No. You were a rogue, no doubt about it. You delighted in embarrassing me every chance you got, and I guess I made an easy target. But there was always that chivalrous side of you. No one ever messed with Patsy, because that meant they'd have to deal with you. I'd have given anything to have had someone looking out for me the way you always looked out for her. And then, one day, it happened. You became my guardian angel, too—a bit tarnished around the edges, maybe, but an angel nonetheless.''

"I was hell on wheels, Imogen, and you know it.''

"I know that the night you made love to me was magical. You were,'' she said, glad darkness camouflaged the flush stealing over her face, "a wonderful lover.''

"As if you'd have known the difference!''

Her flush deepened at the way he dismissed her. "If it makes you feel better to trivialize the whole incident, go ahead, Joe. But nothing you say changes the fact that you're the one who taught me what passion and desire were all about.''

"If I did, princess,'' he said, "it's because I'd had plenty of practice. You probably still believed in the tooth fairy when I got laid for the first time.''

"Resorting to vulgarity won't change anything, either,'' she snapped. "Deny it all you like, but the plain truth is that I felt like a piece of dirt after Philip Maitland got through with me, and it took you to restore my sense of self-worth. You turned a horrible experience around and made me feel beautiful for the first time in my life. And don't bother telling me I don't know what I'm talking about, because I do.''

''You don't know diddly squat, Imogen. You've just come down with a bad case of wishful thinking—that, or your memory's playing tricks on you.''

''I'd have been inclined to agree before I found the diary.''

''What diary?''

''The one I started writing the day I turned fifteen. I came across it in my room. You'd be surprised at how often your name crops up.''

''Do us both a favor and burn the damned thing,'' he said.

''It's too late.''

''Too late for what? Or don't I want to know?''

''It won't change what's happening now. The connection we both thought had been broken when we each left town nine years ago is still there between us, Joe. The other day, you said that you wanted to finish the last chapter of the book where you and I were concerned. Well, the way I see it, it hasn't been written yet.''

He took a long curve too fast and sent her swinging toward the passenger door. ''I don't like the way your mind's working,'' he said. ''You'll be throwing out the L-word, next.''

''No. It's too soon for that, and I know it, but it's a distinct possibility.''

''Not for me, it isn't. It'll never happen.''

Her heart fell a little at the certainty in his voice.

"Well, I can only speak for myself, of course, but I don't see what's so impossible about you and I..."

He expelled a sigh of pure frustration and thumped his fist on the steering wheel. "Would you change your mind if I told you that I spent three years in jail for killing a man?"

"Only three years?" she asked, refusing to let him shock her into retreat. "Then you must have been falsely accused."

"Nice try, princess, but you're way off the mark. A man died and I killed him. With my bare hands."

"Why?"

"What the hell does it matter why? I took a life and was thrown in jail."

"Where?"

"What is this, twenty questions? On Ojo del Diablo, an island off the coast of Colombia."

Diablo. Devil. Despite the warm night, gooseflesh prickled her skin. "It sounds rather forbidding."

"It was a place right out of hell. The name means devil's eye. A few residents claimed it referred to the lake in the center of the island, but the most popular belief was that the place was damned and the devil's eye followed you wherever you went."

"How did you wind up there?"

"By accident."

Clearly, he did not intend to be forthcoming. Normally, she'd have respected his privacy. But in view of the way he'd invaded hers, she felt a little reciprocity was justified. "Okay, Joe, what's the real story here? Because you can't seriously expect me to believe that you just went out and killed a man for the fun of it."

"Go to blazes, Imogen! I've never been big on spilling my guts, and this particular subject is something I'd just as soon forget about.''

"You brought it up," she pointed out, reasonably.

But he reacted with an anger she'd never seen in him. "Because I want you off my back!" he snarled. "You and I don't fit, no matter how much you try to jam the pieces into place. I'm not interested in playing the lead in your 'Princess and the Jailbird' soap opera.''

"And I'm not interested in judging your past." When his only response was to stare stonily ahead, she placed a tentative hand on his arm. "It's the man you are today that counts, Joe. Surely you know that?''

Even in the gloom, she saw his grimace of distaste. "It's the man you are today that counts!" he echoed in an insulting falsetto. "Good golly, Miss Imogen, I pity the guy who winds up married to you! Sitting across the table from a woman who takes a bromide pill before breakfast every morning would be a hell of a way to start the day.''

He took sarcasm to new heights. "Please don't lose any sleep over the idea that I'm about to propose," she said huffily. "In fact, if the main objective of your diatribe is to persuade me you're the last man in the world I should be trying to corral, you're succeeding admirably. The longer this conversation goes on, the more convinced I'm becoming that you're right. Beyond the fact that we made a baby, you and I really don't have a single thing in common.''

A sign posting the approach to Rosemont flashed by. "Well, praise the lord!" he crowed jubilantly. "It's taken nearly two hours, but she finally got the message.''

"You can deny it all you like, but two hours ago, you wanted nothing more than to make love to me.''

"Sure I did. Any man would. You're a lovely woman.

It's how you react to the idea that bothers me. You're convinced you're still carrying a torch for me. And why? Because I know what you're wearing under that modest jacket and skirt. Tell me, Imogen, how many men can say the same? How many others have seen you naked and taken you to bed?''

She turned away from him, afraid that if she tried to answer, she'd betray her utter ignorance of anything approaching the intimacy she'd shared with him.

But he knew. ''I thought as much,'' he said. ''Not a one. Your Puritan little soul won't forgive you for having conceived a child out of wedlock, and the only way you can earn redemption is by making yourself miserable all over again. Because that's what would happen if you were stuck with me, princess. I'm not the country club, round-of-golf type, and I never will be.''

''Is that what this is all about?'' she said. ''Whether or not you belong to the right clubs?''

He sighed like a man whose patience was being tried beyond mortal capacity. ''Do you know what I do for a living? I train horses for a friend of the expat American who got me off Ojo del Diablo. I live in a one-bedroom house on a spread in the foothills of the Cuyamaca Mountains in California and come home at the end of the day with manure stuck to my boots.

''And you want to know what else? I love it. Not because I've made more money than I ever expected to or because my boss respects me and values my work, but because it makes me happy. And the woman who marries me is going to have to be content with that and what I'm able to provide for her. No foreign sports cars, no mansion on the hill and only a very modest diamond on her finger.''

"I don't need a rich man," she said in a small voice. "I have enough money of my own."

"And I don't want to be kept by a woman. So go back to the big city and find yourself a man who fits the mold, princess."

"In other words, even if I'd told you about the baby and she hadn't died, I'd still have had to cope on my own."

"I didn't say that. But we're not dealing with what if, we're dealing with what is."

Yes, they were, and if sex was all he had to bring to their relationship, she was better off without him.

He'd barely brought the car to a stop outside Deepdene before she opened the door and stepped out. "Don't bother," she said, when he made a move to do likewise. "I can make it the rest of the way without you."

There was a pause before he slammed his door closed and his voice floated into the night, underscored by the muted growl of the engine as he shifted into first gear. "That's what I've been trying to tell you all along, princess. But don't take it to mean that I don't intend to do a little research into our daughter's whereabouts, because I do. And if you're still interested in finding the baby's grave—"

"I'm not," she said. "At least, not with you. In fact, the less I have to do with you, the better. And just for the record, you're the one who came chasing after me, following me along the boardwalk, showing up at my hotel, phoning me at my mother's house and asking me out tonight, not the other way around. If I'd had my way, we'd never have exchanged another word after I left you and Patsy at the restaurant in the park two evenings ago."

As a parting shot, it found its mark. He roared off down the drive in a screech of tires, leaving behind nothing but the smell of burning rubber. A savvy woman would have let that be enough to solace the wounds he'd inflicted.

But what did she do? Crept to her room and climbed into bed with that infernal diary. As if, since she couldn't have the man himself, she'd make do with the vicarious thrills of reliving past experiences with him.

May 21

Played tennis at the club with Rick Aldren this p.m. Temperature must have been in the nineties. He drove me home after. Stopped on the way to get gas at Donnelly's Garage. Joe was lending a hand, dressed for the weather, stripped to the waist and wearing denim cutoffs that looked about ready to fall off. Talk about tall and tanned! I couldn't take my eyes off him. He came over to clean the bugs off the windshield and I practically drooled at the sight. Even his armpits are sexy. He saw me looking and gave me that smile of his....

December 21

Tonight was the best night of my life. I talked Mother into letting me go to the Christmas social at St. Patrick's Church and Joe Donnelly was playing in the band. Of course, I had an earlier curfew than anyone else and was on my way out of the hall just as he was coming back from a break, and we bumped into each other. We both looked up and saw the mistletoe and of course I blushed. And he smiled the way he always does and said, "Well, princess, I guess this is where you get to kiss the frog. Merry Christmas." And he kissed me. Not just one of those peck-on-the-cheek things, but a real lip slammer, as Julie Coombs would say.

I'll never forget how it felt, sort of soft and firm all at the same time. None of that spit and tooth tangling business Dave Baxter goes in for. But then, he hasn't had much practice, whereas everybody knows Joe Donnelly's been kissing girls practically from the day he started kindergarten.

Saturday, March 14

Dear Diary, this is the first time I've been able to write anything down since my father died last month. I miss him so much. I can't believe I'll never see him again or hear his voice. Mother says life goes on and we have to make the best of it, but sometimes I wonder why, if all a person has to look forward to is dying. I haven't been out much. Don't really feel like seeing anyone. At school, people don't seem to know what to say to me, although my friends do their best to cheer me up. But then this afternoon I went into town to get my hair cut and ran into Joe Donnelly as I was leaving the salon. Usually, all he does is smirk and make some smart remark but today he stopped and said he was sorry to hear about my father and how was I doing. Actually, I'd been feeling as if some sort of fire had gone out inside me, but the way he spoke, as if he really cared and wasn't just going through the motions, brought a little flicker of warmth back to life.

July 26

Maureen Wallace invited a whole gang of us over to her place for a barbecue yesterday and I had a great time until I burned my hand flipping hamburgers.

Patsy, ever the nurse-in-waiting, took me to her house for first aid.

Mrs. Donnelly was in the kitchen taking fruit pies out of the oven. She sat at the table next to me and fussed about putting cream on my blister.

Just as she finished bandaging my hand, Joe came into the house and suddenly that big, homey kitchen seemed small and cramped. He was stripped to the waist and after I stopped staring at his muscles and the hair on his chest, I noticed he was carrying a puppy wrapped up in his shirt. He'd found the poor thing lying abandoned at the side of the road outside town. He found a box and blanket and fed the puppy some milk, then came and straddled a chair across from me and said I looked almost as miserable as the mutt and hadn't my mother ever told me not to play with fire.

He made me feel really weird inside. All tingly and full, as if I might throw up, then hot and churning and achy.

I know from things Julie Coombs talks about that boys like to touch girls' breasts and even touch other parts of their bodies, but it's never happened to me, nor have I ever wanted it to. Actually, the whole idea seemed gross and disgusting before. But something's changed and all I know is that, if Joe Donnelly had suggested I go with him down by the river, I would have walked out of that house without a backward glance and let him touch anything he wanted....

And eleven years later, nothing much had changed.

*   *   *

"I was hoping you'd stop by my room for a little chat last night, but I suppose you were too tired."

Suzanne let the remark drop casually at breakfast the next morning, but Imogen recognized it as the opening salvo in what would surely amount to the fiercest clash of wills she'd yet to engage in with her mother. Of course, it was bound to happen sooner or later. But later would have been nice—after, rather than before, the first cup of coffee of the day.

Stalling, and despising herself for doing so, she said, "It was late when I got back."

"I noticed." The fractional silence, the small, disparaging sniff, spoke volumes of disapproval. Installed behind the silver coffeepot, her morning robe falling in graceful folds of red silk from her throat to her ankles, with every last shining blond hair perfectly in place, Suzanne clearly thought she had the situation very well in hand. She captured a sugar cube in sterling tongs and held it poised over her cup much like an executioner about to lower the ax. "I have to say, Imogen, I was shocked—shocked—that you agreed to be seen with that man yesterday. Have you forgotten it was he who ruined your life?"

"That's enough, Mother. I don't want to hear this."

"Well, someone certainly has to make you see the folly of your ways, and who better than your mother? Or have you forgotten that it was I who came to the rescue when you found yourself in trouble? Furthermore, how you can defend a man you must surely despise—"

"I said I don't want to hear this, Mother, so please stop it right now."

The sugar cube dropped into the cup with an affronted little plop. "I'm not sure I care for your tone, Imogen. In fact, I don't like it one little bit."

"I'm sorry. But if my being somewhat abrupt—"

"Abrupt?" With meticulous care, Suzanne raised the cup to her lips and took a sip. "You're being downright rude."

Gazing steadily at her mother, Imogen stood her ground. "If that's the only way I can get what I have to say across to you, then I'm afraid you'll just have to put up with it. Because for once, Mother, I'm going to talk and you're going to listen. And if," she said, raising her hand to override the outburst she could see was about to erupt, "you cannot, or will not, do that, then I shall leave this house yet again, and this time I won't be coming back."

She paused, as much to gauge the effect she'd had on her mother as to draw breath. Suzanne sat transfixed, her china blue eyes sparking aggrievedly, but she uttered not a word.

Encouraged, Imogen continued. "First of all, I do not despise Joe Donnelly."

But I ache for him and what might have been!

The truth attacked without warning, a vicious stab of regret that punctured her composure. It was her own fault. She should never have opened that blasted diary again.

Resolutely gearing her thoughts to the here and now, she picked up where she'd left off. "Whether or not you care to acknowledge the fact, he was your grandchild's father, which, in itself, is a tie that will always bind me to him. When I was a girl of eighteen, you were perhaps right to interfere in my life, and I'm sure you thought you were acting in my best interests. But I'm not a girl any longer. I took charge of my life a long time ago."

She stopped to finish her juice—a risky move since it gave her mother the opportunity to jump in and try to seize control of the conversation—but Suzanne appeared to be in a state of shock and stared at her across the table.

"I had no other choice, Mother, because you'd washed your hands of me, and there was no one else I could to turn to. And let's not pretend you did this all for my own good, because you were thinking of what was best for you, too. You were ashamed of me, and I think you were glad that my baby died, because heaven only knows how you'd have explained her to your friends."

Beyond a strangled gasp, Suzanne offered no comment.

"But I was devastated at losing her, not just because she was my daughter, but because she was also Joe's and all I had left of him. You might have been able to put her out of your mind, but I never could, and you can have no idea how often I've wondered how things might have turned out for us if she had lived and Joe had known about her."

She stopped and pretended to busy herself buttering a slice of toast. In reality, she was close to tears—again. It was something that had been happening with drab monotony practically from the moment she'd arrived in town. The reason this time was that, from her perspective, life with Joe and their baby could have been pretty wonderful. The pity of it was, he didn't see things in quite the same light.

Suzanne stirred. "I cannot imagine—"

"Please let me finish, Mother, then I'll be more than happy to let you say your piece. First of all, I realize that there's no going back, and if you're worried that Joe and I might resume our relationship, you can relax because he's made it crystal clear it's not going to happen. But that doesn't make him the villain of the piece, nor was he ever the bad person you tried to make him out to be. He was devastated to learn there'd been a baby and that she'd died.''

"You told him?'' The question ghosted past her mother's lips frail as thistledown. "Imogen, what on earth possessed you?''

"Actually, he confronted me with the truth and I wasn't about to lie. Naturally, he had questions.''

"Don't answer them. He has no right—''

"He has every right. That's why he asked me out last night, to get answers. But there was very little I could tell him beyond the bare facts, and that's not enough to satisfy him.''

"Oh, the man should be shot!'' Suzanne exclaimed. "Can't you see that he's bringing back all the pain you suffered as if it happened just yesterday? Stay away from him, Imogen, please.''

"He can't just file his child's death away like an old tax return. More to the point, neither can I.'' Pushing her plate aside, Imogen leaned across the table urgently. "For years, I've refused to confront those questions, but they haven't gone away because I ignored them, Mother. They're still gnawing away at the back of my mind, and it's taken Joe to make me realize they always will be unless I deal with them.''

Taking a deep breath, she leveled a very direct look at Suzanne. "So, tell me, Mother, where can we find the birth records and where is our daughter buried? Because Joe is anxious to learn everything there is to know about her and to visit her grave. And for both our sakes, I've agreed to help him.''

"*No!*'' Hoarsely, the cry burst from Suzanne at the same time that her coffee cup slipped out of her hand

and spread its contents over the polished surface of the table. "My God, Imogen, you cannot let him pursue this matter!"

"I couldn't stop him even if I tried. We're not dealing with a frightened teenager here. Joe Donnelly's a man with a mind and a will of his own. He's determined to assert his rights, and I can't say I blame him. I had no business keeping the pregnancy from him in the first place."

Suzanne's face seemed to cave in on itself. The woman who, half an hour earlier, could have passed for a well-preserved forty-five suddenly looked an unhealthy seventy. "Imogen," she whispered, raising a palsied hand to her throat, "I'm begging you, for all our sakes, put a stop to this before it goes any further."

"You're overreacting." Though outwardly calm in the face of such an impassioned outburst, Imogen was thoroughly alarmed. "Why should I try to put him off?"

Her mother might have been staring into the jaws of hell when she replied. "Because there is no grave, Imogen. The child did not die."

CHAPTER EIGHT

LISTER'S Meadows didn't look so very different from the way it had the last time Imogen had seen it, the day she'd burned her hand on the barbecue. Children still played under laundry hanging from long lines in the back gardens, geraniums grew in pots on windowsills, and bright gold and orange nasturtiums spilled over the low wall fronting the Donnelly house. Even the dog dozing in the sun on the doorstep looked like an older version of the puppy Joe had brought home that day she'd been seventeen and disillusionment was still a year away.

She paused on the road, glad she'd parked her car at the store on the corner. The rented Lincoln would have announced the arrival of a stranger louder than a trumpet call, and she dearly needed time to compose herself, to rehearse for the fiftieth time how she was going to share the bombshell that had landed in her lap that morning.

In the wake of her mother's revelation, the air in the morning room had grown still, breathless, so heavy and thick it was all Imogen's heart could do to labor on. "What did you say?" she'd whispered.

"Your child did not die, my dear—but it was better that you thought she did."

"Better for whom, Mother?" she'd cried in anguish. "For me? For Joe? Or for you?"

"For everyone, including her," Suzanne had replied, and when Imogen pressured her for more information, had reluctantly admitted, "She was adopted and is being well taken care of."

Beyond that, however, she refused to go.

Imogen's frustration knew no bounds. Shock, elation, anger and bewilderment had rendered her incapable of coherent thought. The questions had hammered inside her head, shrieking to be heard—who, where, when? But, overriding them all and refusing to be silenced, *why?*

Eventually she'd found her answer, and the full tragedy had revealed itself. "Because," Suzanne had said, weeping, "she was the product of rape. Every time you looked at your child, you would have been reminded of the violence from which she'd sprung. How could you live like that? And how could I allow such a blight to remain with you?"

Imogen had stared at her mother, stunned. "What in the world are you talking about? Joe didn't rape me. Do you hear me, Mother? He did not rape me."

"Imogen, I found your dress, all torn and filthy. I saw the bruises on your neck and arms."

"He was not the one responsible for that," Imogen had protested, appalled.

"You have blocked it all out of your mind because you cannot bear to remember, but I shall never forget. Or forgive. I wrestled with my conscience at the time, oh, my dear, I truly did. He should have been brought to justice for the crime he committed against you. But you were so young, Imogen—my little girl, your father's precious child—and I could not bring myself to expose you or our fine family name to the public humiliation legal action would have precipitated."

"So instead of asking me what really happened, you shipped me away." For the life of her, Imogen hadn't been able to control the bitter edge in her voice. "Out of sight, out of mind. Was that it, Mother?"

"A change of scene, Paris in July—it seemed the best remedy at the time and could scarcely be construed as punishment."

"And later, when you realized I was pregnant and sent me to live with your cousin Amy, was that also not to be construed as punishment?"

Her mother had wilted in her chair, an old, faded rose no longer able to hold its petals together. "I don't know! I did what I thought was best. How could I have known that, almost ten years later, you'd resume a relationship with a man you had every reason to despise? How could I know you'd be so foolish as to tell him there had been a baby? And as for his wanting to visit his daughter's grave, who in her right mind would find such a gesture admirable? He is as much a scoundrel without conscience today as he was the night he took you by force for his own gratification. Or are you going to look at me with those big accusing eyes and tell me he did not rob you of your innocence?"

"He made love to me."

"Love?" Suzanne had echoed indignantly. "You call that love? Then you are a bigger fool that I thought."

A movement at the front door drew Imogen to the moment and the mission at hand. Mrs. Donnelly had come out to sweep her front porch. The dog stretched and rolled over. The sun blazed on the nasturtiums and on the brick-lined path leading to the house and on the little brass letter box hanging on the wall.

Imogen knew what she had to do would not be easy. To her shame, she briefly considered not sharing the news with Joe. What was the point? Why burden him with knowledge he couldn't act on? They hardly had the right to search out their child and demand that her adoptive family return her to her birth parents, after all.

And anyway, a small, mean-spirited voice had whispered, *since he's made it so clear that he doesn't want anything to do with you, why fly in the face of his rejection?*

Because the trail of deceit has gone on too long already and has to end here, her conscience had replied severely. *And because he's been falsely accused. And because it's my responsibility to put things right.*

Aware that she had a visitor, Mrs. Donnelly stopped sweeping and shaded her eyes with one hand. "Good heavens, is that you, Imogen?"

"That's right." Smiling, Imogen bent to pat the dog's head. "I didn't expect you'd remember me. How are you, Mrs. Donnelly?"

"Well, lovey, I'm just fine. And you're looking wonderful. But then, you always did. Come along in out of the heat. I expect it's Patsy you've come to see."

"Actually," Imogen said, following her down a narrow hall to the kitchen at the back, "I was hoping to have a word with Joe."

"With Joe, you say?" Mrs. Donnelly eyed her keenly. "Well, he's not here just at this moment. Drove the Thunderbird back to Sean's, he did, but he'll be home any minute. Patsy and I were just about to take a coffee break. Thought we'd sit under the apple tree out back, where it's cool. Will you join us while you're waiting, lovey?"

A screen door slammed on the back porch and Patsy, looking no more than seventeen in shorts and a halter top, appeared. "Imogen, for heaven's sake, what a nice surprise! I looked for you in the tea tent at the school yesterday afternoon, but someone said you left right after the ceremony.''

''Well, she's here now, so you can catch up on the news while she waits for Joe. Here, Pats, carry the tray and I'll bring the coffee.''

''You're waiting to see Joe?'' Patsy said warily as they paraded across the grass to the dappled shade of the apple tree. ''Did he know you were stopping by?''

''No.'' Imogen cast a glance at Mrs. Donnelly, so warmly at ease, so hospitable, and wondered how she'd react to the news that she'd been denied knowledge of one of her grandchildren. Would her unflappable good nature extend to forgiving such an omission?

''Have you, um, spent any time with him since you've been home?'' Patsy asked, her manner positively furtive.

''Some. We had dinner together last night and visited for a couple of hours the night before that. Why?''

''Because—oh, heck, Imogen, I told him something I should have kept to myself, and it's been eating me alive ever since.'' She grimaced and blew out a long, unhappy breath. ''You'll probably never speak to me again when I tell you.''

Suddenly, Imogen knew. Joe and Patsy had always been close. Add that to her present distress and the way she was twisting her paper napkin to shreds, and it didn't take a genius to come up with the right answer. ''You somehow found out about my pregnancy and told Joe, didn't you?''

The famous Donnelly eyes seemed even bluer against the brilliant flush staining Patsy's face. ''I'm so ashamed, Imogen, I could die. I know it was unethical, and you have my solemn word I'll never breathe a word to another living soul, and I know Joe won't, either. I wouldn't even have told him now, except he seemed so—''

''So what, Pats?'' His voice cut through the confession like hot steel through butter. He'd come around the house without their noticing and stood behind them, leaning against the trunk of the apple tree, his arms folded across his chest and his gaze an outright challenge.

Patsy gave a yelp and sprang out of her chair as if she'd suddenly found herself sitting on a hornet's nest. No matter which way she turned, she was cornered.

Realizing something was seriously amiss, Mrs. Donnelly stood with the coffeepot in one hand and an empty mug in the other. ''What's all the fuss about?''

''Patsy's cleansing her soul at everyone else's expense,'' Joe said. ''Go on, Pats. Finish what you were saying.''

Miserably, Patsy searched for an avenue of escape and found none. ''I...''

''Have you been spreading gossip?'' her mother asked reproachfully. ''Why, Patsy Donnelly, I thought I'd brought you up to know better!''

Imogen couldn't stand by silently a moment longer. Her own burden of knowledge weighed too heavily for her to have the heart or energy to condemn anyone else. ''It wasn't gossip. It was something Joe had a right to know, and I should have told him years ago. I'm grateful to you, Patsy, for tackling what I was too cowardly to face.''

Patsy promptly burst into tears.

''Well,'' Mrs. Donnelly said, taking her by the elbow, ''since we know Imogen came here to see Joe and not us, we're going to make ourselves scarce and leave them to sort out whatever troubles they've got without any more help from you, Patricia Mary Louise.''

Joe waited until they'd disappeared inside the house before swinging his gaze to Imogen. ''Well, what gives?''

''I came to see you.''

''So I gather.'' He shifted irritably and shoved himself away from the tree. ''Why? What's up?''

''We need to talk.''

He flung her a look of unutterable weariness. ''I'm all talked out, Imogen. So if you're still insisting on trying to cobble together the remnants of what you fondly believe to have been the romance of a lifetime, you're wasting your time. I thought I made that clear last night.''

''That's not why I'm here.''

''Well, good. Because I'm beginning to find this whole business tiresome. You're a nice woman, an attractive woman, and I'd be more than happy to have a fling with you if you were anyone but who you are. But as things stand, the—''

''Our daughter is alive, Joe.''

If dramatic effect was what she'd been aiming for, she couldn't have timed the announcement better. For a second, the silence was deafening. Then, dazed, he muttered, ''Say that again.''

''Our daughter is alive.''

''Since when?''

''Since my mother admitted it to me this morning.''

He slumped into one of the lawn chairs. ''What the hell kind of game are the two of you playing here, Imogen?''

''No game, I promise you. At least, not on my part.''

''Oh, yeah?'' His gaze probed her face, seeking the

lies he was so sure she was concealing. "You'll be telling me next that she's been hidden away in the attic all this time."

"No. She was adopted."

"*What?* Who—"

"I have no idea."

"How bloody convenient! Just enough information to keep me hanging around begging for more! You don't seriously expect me to believe all this, do you?"

"I expect you to focus on what's important here. I've just told you that the child we thought had died is alive. I'm halfway between heaven and hell, my stomach's in knots, I don't know whether to laugh or cry, and you think it's all some sort of devious game. What's wrong with you, Joe Donnelly?"

"Gee, I don't know," he sneered. "Maybe it's got something to do with the fact that, ever since we ran into each other again, you've managed to keep me so off balance that I don't know what to expect next. First I find out from someone else that I fathered a child."

"You found out from Patsy, as you very well know."

"Big deal!" He waved that aside as being of no consequence. "When you can't wriggle away from that truth, you trade on my sympathies by giving me some cockamamie story about the baby having died. I ask for details, and you can't tell me a damn thing—no reason for the death, no birth records, nothing. The past is over, you tell me. It's the future that counts."

"It is!"

"But not with me, princess. I've already spelled it out. The only way we'd ever have headed down the same road is if the baby had lived. So now what do we have?" Grabbing a couple of forks, he rattled them on the tray in a fair imitation of a drumroll. "Surprise, folks! The man isn't off the hook, after all. The daughter he thought was dead and buried just turned up alive and well.''

''I know how you must feel. I—''

''I feel screwed around! I feel like a goddamned fool! And I want to know what other schemes you're hatching.'' He nailed her in a glower. ''How many more alligators are swimming around in that pond you call a brain?''

She traded him glare for glare. ''If your chief concern is that you're going to find yourself saddled with me despite your best efforts to escape the net you seem to think I'm casting, let me ease your mind. This may come as a shock to a man who obviously has an inordinately high opinion of his charms, but the more I see of you, the less attractive I find you.

''As for the schemes you correctly assume I'm hatching—well, brace yourself, Joe, because here comes another blow to that massive ego. They don't concern you. I've got more important missions in mind. For instance, I want to see my child. I want to know that she's happy and healthy. I want to know if the people she's living with have enough money to give her the kind of life she needs and deserves. If they haven't, then I hope they'll allow me to help them out. Regardless, I intend to set up a trust fund for her future.''

She stopped because she'd run out of breath.

He immediately took advantage and jumped in with both feet. ''You're going to try to buy her, you mean. As if that'll make up for the fact that you let your mother—'' he ground his teeth and fairly spat the word out ''—trample all over that baby's right to know her own parents.''

''You could put it that way, I suppose, if you lacked the charity to view my actions in a kinder light.'' She stood and faced him, head held high. "I'm tired of trying to change your mind about me, Joe. Think what you like. I no longer give a royal hoot."

She was halfway to the house before he caught up with her. "Just where the hell do you think you're going?" he asked, hauling her unceremoniously to a stop.

"To start searching." Pointedly, she looked at the long fingers clamped around her wrist. "Kindly let go of my arm. I've wasted enough time on you."

The breath hissed between his lips. His eyes sparked blue fury. "*We* will start searching, princess. Together. And we'll begin with Mother Dearest. How'd you get here?"

"By car," she retorted. "Did you think I swooped in on a broomstick?"

"As long as you've got transportation and we can get a move on, I really don't give a damn."

Suzanne had recovered sufficient poise to change from her morning robe to a tailored blue two-piece. Pale but composed, she stood in the doorway to her sitting room, triple string of pearls in place, hair immaculate, lipstick perfect.

She said nothing when she saw Joe. Instead, with a faint lift of her delicately arched brows, she turned to Imogen. Only her tightly knotted hands betrayed her agitation.

"He knows," Imogen said, in response to her mother's inquiring look. "I passed on to him everything you told me, but I think you know that it isn't nearly enough. We both deserve to hear the rest."

"I suppose you do, but not here," Suzanne replied sharply. "Come into the sunroom where we won't be overheard."

She turned and left Imogen and Joe to follow her to the solarium. Only when the doors were securely closed did she face Joe. "You may be seated, Mr. Donnelly."

"I prefer to stand."

"As you wish." She chose a sofa as far away from him as possible, perched on the arm and regarded him regally. "Well, fire away. No doubt you have plenty to say."

"Right now," he said, "I'm more interested in hearing what you have to say."

She stood and with a shrug moved to a gardenia flowering in a jardiniere. "To you?" she said, and plucked a dead bloom from a stem before looking him in the eye. "Nothing. I owe you neither explanation nor apology. Anything I have done I did for my daughter and I harbor not a single regret. Her best interests were all that concerned me."

He ate up the distance separating them in two strides. "And my daughter's best interests are all that concern me now, so let's cut to the chase. I want to know where she is—and don't bother saying you don't know, because it won't wash."

"She is living in a loving and stable home, and that is all I intend telling you." In a final gesture of defiance, Suzanne tossed the dead bloom onto the soil covering the plant's roots. *There, that is what I think of you and your demands!*

He looked from her to the crumpled flower and back, tucked his hands into the back pockets of his jeans and took a leisurely turn about the room. He stopped to gaze out the south window. Just when Imogen thought she'd scream at the tension-filled atmosphere, he circled until he stood directly in front of Suzanne.

Then he stooped so his eyes were level with hers and,

in a voice so deadly that even Suzanne flinched, said, "Do you think that I am going to let you get away with playing God again? Do you really think you're going to kick me out of your front door as if I were some unwashed vagrant begging for scraps, the way you did the day I came and asked to be allowed to see Imogen, nine summers ago?"

Imogen watched, hypnotized, as the war dance unfolded between her mother and Joe. At this revelation, she let out a smothered exclamation. "Mother? Is that true?"

"Yes," Suzanne said, her gaze never flickering from Joe's. "The pity of it is, I didn't kick him hard enough to deter him from coming back."

Joe smiled, and Imogen thought she had never seen him look more beautiful or more ruthless. His claim that he'd killed a man with his bare hands no longer struck her as an absurd overstatement. Yet despite the threat he presented, his voice was as deceptively mild as a cat's contented purr when he said, "I'm your granddaughter's father. Is that any way to talk about family?"

"I will die before I admit you as a member of this family."

His smile broadened, making the hair on the back of Imogen's neck stand up. "You're in danger of dying even sooner than that, because I'm going to wring your scrawny neck if you don't tell me where my daughter is."

For long seconds, the two adversaries engaged in a standoff. Eyeball to eyeball, they faced each other, but Suzanne's indignation was no match for Joe's implacable anger. For the second time that day, she crumpled, sagging onto the sofa as if her legs had been knocked out from under her. "That won't be necessary."

The seconds spun out, measured by the uneven splash of the fountain outside, by the heavy thud of Imogen's heart, by the rhythmic clenching and relaxing of Joe's fists. "We're waiting," he said in that same soft, deadly tone. "And I'm running out of patience. Where is she, old woman?"

Suzanne raised her hand, then lowered it in a feeble gesture of defeat. "She is a day student at a very good school in Norbury, which, as you might know, lies just west of Niagara Falls."

The name triggered a memory in Imogen's mind. Of course! The canceled check to St. Martha's, which she'd stumbled on in her mother's desk—when? Mere days ago. Or was it in another lifetime, one that revolved around work and friends, around dinner dates, the theater, long ski weekends and all those other components that form the structure of a successful single woman's social calendar?

What did it matter? She was no longer that person. She was a mother again and, within a very few hours, might well lay eyes on her child for the first time! Where would she find the patience to wait so long?

Unaware of Imogen's agitation, Suzanne smoothed the thumb of one hand over the knuckles of the other, then lifted her gaze to Joe. "We do not like each other, Mr. Donnelly, and I doubt that we ever will, but I am not the ogress you paint me to be. In trying to protect my daughter, I did not abandon yours. I have cared for her the best way I knew how without compromising Imogen's chance to put a most unhappy and unfortunate incident behind her and go forward to make a fresh start elsewhere. Perhaps I was wrong. I might even have misjudged you, and if that is so, then I am deeply sorry."

He made no secret of his disgust. "The apology

comes too late, Mrs. Palmer. Nothing you've done makes up for the fact that Imogen and I have lost eight years of our child's life.''

"No. But at least you can pick up the thread now."

"Oh, I doubt that," he snapped. "Your coming clean at this stage hardly entitles either of us to bang on some couple's door and demand to have our daughter turned over to us. How in God's name do we wrench her away from the only family she's ever known? How do we justify having left it this long to announce ourselves? And how do we prove to complete strangers that we are who we claim to be? Answer me those questions, and I might feel more disposed to accept your apology.''

A spark of Suzanne's normal fire reasserted itself. "If I thought it would help, I'd let you have your pound of flesh, Mr. Donnelly, but I think a more useful alternative might be if I were to tell you that the problems you foresee are not as insurmountable as you might expect. The woman I entrusted with my granddaughter's care is no stranger to Imogen. She is the same woman who looked after her when she was a child.''

Imogen stared at her mother openmouthed.

"Yes, Imogen." Suzanne nodded. "I'm talking about Mona Wyborn, your old nanny. She's the one who took your baby and gave her a home.''

Finally, Imogen found her voice. "I thought she was dead, too," she said, and then, to her dismay, she began laughing and couldn't stop. Cackle upon cackle rolled out and echoed around the high-ceilinged solarium. She sounded, she thought, clamping a hand over mouth, as shrill as an old hen trying feebly to lay one last egg.

"Shut up, Imogen," Joe said.

"I can't," she spluttered, collapsing onto the nearest sofa. "I mailed her Christmas cards for years, you see, and they always came back unopened and marked *return to sender,* just like in the song.'' The laughter choked her again, and tears gushed from her eyes. ''Isn't that funny, Joe?''

''No,'' he said, and hauled her into his arms. ''Hush, now, sweetheart. You'll scare the pants off her if we go looking for our daughter with you in this state.''

''Well, I don't see why. At least she'll know I'm happy to see her.'' Except that wasn't true because the laughter had died, and to her dismay, she realized she was sobbing against his shoulder as if her heart would break.

''I'll order some tea,'' her mother said.

''Do that,'' Joe replied, as if he was the master of the house.

It was enough to start the hen trying to lay all over again. But he put a stop to that by stroking her spine over and over until, at last, the hiccupping sobs subsided and she could draw breath again.

Limp and unaccountably exhausted, she leaned into his embrace. She could have stayed like that forever, soaking up the comfort she found in his touch and the wonderful sense of belonging that came from being held in his arms. But he put a stop to that, too, and held her away from him.

''Feeling better?''

''Actually—'' she sniffled ''—I feel rather ridiculous. I don't know what came over me.''

''It doesn't take a rocket scientist to figure that one out, Imogen. You've been on an emotional roller coaster practically from the minute you set foot in town, and you're exhausted.''

She looked up and saw the concern in his eyes.

"Don't look so worried, Joe. I'll be fine. The worst is over."

"Do you think so?" he asked. "My guess is, it's only just begun."

"How can you say that? Our little girl is alive." Her smile started at the corners of her mouth and spread until every part of her body felt bathed by its warmth. "Think about it! In a few hours we'll meet her. See her, speak to her, touch her."

"And then what?"

"I don't know. I can't think any further ahead than that."

"I hate to burst your bubble, princess, but—"

"Then don't." She shook her head and pressed her hand against his mouth. "Right now, today is all I can deal with. Please don't ask me to worry about tomorrow."

He held her gaze a moment longer, then let out a sigh and kissed her fingertips. "Okay, Imogen, have it your way. But don't delude yourself this is going to be any sort of picnic. We're about to turn at least two lives upside-down. Make sure you save enough strength to deal with the consequences."

CHAPTER NINE

THE house sat in the curve of a quiet crescent, with a neat patch of lawn behind a white picket fence and green shutters framing the windows. The roof was steeply gabled, the walls whitewashed brick. A stone-paved path meandered from the gate to where tall red hollyhocks stood sentinel beside the front door. The only thing missing from the postcard-perfect picture was a fat tabby cat snoozing in the afternoon sun.

"Well, here goes." Joe glanced at the house, then at her. "Are you ready for this?"

Was she? She didn't know. Her hands were wet, the palms imprinted with the dents made by her nails. Her stomach felt hollow with expectation at the same time that fear left a metallic aftertaste on her tongue.

Joe peered at her suspiciously. "You're not going to go strange on me again, are you?"

She didn't answer. Her attention was drawn to the woman who'd appeared from around the side of the house. Wiping her palms on the apron tied around her middle, she approached the visitors. Her hair was grayer than Imogen remembered, her face more lined, her hands more worn, but her smile hadn't changed. She even smelled the same, of old English lavender laced with starch, and although Imogen had to stoop to kiss her cheek, she still gave the warmest hugs in the world.

"Well, bless my soul, darling child, you're here at last!" Mona Wyborn crooned, enfolding Imogen to her.

"I've been watching and waiting ever since your mother phoned to let me know you were coming."

"Mother called and told you?"

"Yes. She thought it best that I be prepared." Mona stepped back and mopped unashamedly with her apron at the tears trickling down her face. "Well, just look at you, my baby! All grown-up and as beautiful now as the day you were born. Oh, many's the time I've wanted to get in touch, Imogen. I promised your mother I'd keep her secret, though, and I couldn't go back on my word. But I'm glad you're here now and that you know about Cassie. It's time the truth came out."

Imogen hung onto the gate, her emotions so hopelessly tangled that she didn't know whether to laugh or cry. "Is that what you call her? Cassie?"

"Well, her real name's Cassandra, but it's a big mouthful for a little girl, so everyone calls her Cassie. Except her gran, of course." Eyes twinkling, Mona transferred her attention to Joe, who waited patiently on the sidelines. "I don't imagine I have to tell *you* that Mrs. P.'s a stickler for having things done right."

"No, ma'am, you don't." His smile, so open and warm, left Imogen's heart aching. He'd never shown her such courtly charm. She hadn't known he had it in him. "I got that message loud and clear a long time ago. I'm Joe Donnelly, by the way. Cassie's father."

Mona gave him a hug, too, something he didn't appear to mind one bit. "You don't have to tell me that, young man! The child's the living image of her daddy."

Glancing toward the house, Imogen said, "Is she here, Mona? May we see her?"

"Well, darling, I sent her over to play with a friend." As she spoke, Mona led them to the front door. "I thought it might be easier on everyone not to have her here when you first arrived. But she's not far away, no more than a few houses, and she can be home in five minutes, once you feel ready to face her.''

The front door led into a tiny hall, which opened directly into a large cozy living room filled with chintz-covered sofas and chairs and dark cherry furniture. A spindled staircase hugged one wall, and there was a cat, after all, not a tabby but a snooty Siamese who reclined elegantly on the back of a wing chair beside the fireplace and watched from impassive blue eyes as strangers invaded his territory.

''It isn't much, compared to what you're used to, Imogen,'' Mona said, looking around with pride, ''but it's warm and comfortable in the winter, I have just enough garden to keep me happy in the summer, and I love it. Cassie has her own big room upstairs with a spare bed for a friend, and the school bus picks her up and drops her off at the gate every day. She's been happy here, darling, and I've done my best to bring her up the way you'd want.''

Overcome, Imogen flung her arms around her old nanny a second time. ''Oh, I'm so glad you were the one who looked after her and that you kept her safe for me! As for your house, it's lovely, Mona. Exactly the kind of place I always imagined you'd choose and perfect for a little girl.''

''Well, your mother and I had quite a go-round about that at the time. She was all for moving me into something more 'suitable,' but I dug my heels in. Bad enough, I told her, that I was deceiving you and forbidden to so much as send you a birthday card, and you as dear to me as if you were my own child all those years. Worse, I had to remove all the photos I'd kept of you since you were a baby and hide them away on the top shelf of the closet in my bedroom, so that Cassie wouldn't ask questions. As if that would put a stop to a child's natural curiosity about where she came from!''

''Are you saying she's asked about us?'' Joe asked sharply.

Indicating a door, Mona said, ''Why don't we talk in the kitchen while I make us some tea?''

Painted sunny yellow, the kitchen ran the width of the house, with deep-silled windows looking out on a fenced back garden. Bird feeders hung from the branches of an ancient oak, below which was a stone birdbath.

Mona filled a copper kettle, set it to heat on the stove and lifted a japanned tea caddy from a shelf. ''The thing is,'' she said, ''Cassie's been asking questions for a while now. She's a smart little girl and she sees that the life she has here with me isn't the same as what her friends have.''

Imogen exchanged an anxious glance with Joe. ''What have you told her, Mona?''

''Well, she calls me Nanny, and she knows that the lady who comes to visit once a month is her grandmother who lives in another town. For a long time, that was enough. But lately, she's started asking where her real mommy and daddy are. I've said that sometimes things don't work out the way they're supposed to, but...'' She sighed and flung a sheepish look over her shoulder. ''But that if a person wishes and prays, some day she might get the things she wants.''

''And now some day is here, and we don't have the first idea how to explain why it's taken us so long to show up.'' Too overwrought to remain seated, at the table, Imogen paced nervously to the window.

Joe, on the other hand, seemed completely self-assured. "Calm down, princess. All we can do is play it by ear. The right words'll come, you'll see."

"Easy for you to say," she said scornfully. He thought he had the answers to everything, as, in a way, he had. Because he'd been as much sinned against as his daughter and was in no way to blame for the fact that she'd been denied access to her parents.

Mona watched the robins splashing in the birdbath, turning away only when the kettle let out a shrill whistle. She waited until she'd poured the tea before she said, "Well, I think we all know it's not going to be easy, lovey, but in my opinion, Joe's right. Maybe the best thing we can do is let Cassie come home and meet you, and just leave the rest up to her. She's not a shy child. If she wants to know something, she'll ask. And if you want my advice, the best thing you can do is answer her as honestly as you know how." She paused inquiringly. "Well? Shall I phone and have her come home?"

"Yes," Joe said. "Let's get on with it."

They waited as she dialed a number. Waited as she spoke to someone at the other end. Waited as she hung up.

"She's on her way," Mona said.

They waited some more. A minute? Two? A hundred? The tea sat cooling in the cups.

Then the front gate clanged. Footsteps raced up the path. The front door slammed shut. And the waiting was over.

"I'm afraid," Imogen cried, clutching the edge of the table in a death grip.

Joe nudged her sharply with his elbow. "Don't be ridiculous. We're about to meet our child. What is there to be afraid of?"

How could he be so sure of himself, she wondered, sagging against him. How be so brave?

She was the most beautiful child he'd ever seen. Dark and vivacious, with a gap-toothed smile to steal a man's heart away, and bright blue eyes that looked squarely into his, she fairly danced into the kitchen, a sprite of a girl with her mother's delicate bones and his coloring, both stamped with an individuality that was all her own.

He didn't know when he'd found his chair again, whether he'd fallen into it by accident or chosen to sit on purpose. He didn't remember reaching over to hang on to Imogen's hand like a drowning man clinging to a life ring, or if he managed to stretch his mouth into some sort of smile when his daughter beamed at him delightedly and said hello. But he knew at once that he'd move heaven and earth before he'd let anyone try to cut him out of her life again.

Numbly, he watched Imogen reach over and shake her hand. How the hell did she do it? The kid was her daughter, for crying out loud! How did she stop herself from sweeping her into her arms and smothering her with kisses? How did she keep her smile pinned in place?

They were talking, the three of them. He saw their mouths move, although what came out might as well have been Swahili for all it meant to him. Women's gabble, that's all it was. The kid—no, not kid! Cassie. His daughter. Cassie leaned against her nanny and twined a skinny arm around her waist. He'd have given ten years of his life to have her smile at him like that, as if he'd hung the moon.

Mona Wyborn was a good woman, he had no doubt of that. Her old face was wreathed in love for the girl. But damn it, she was neither mother nor father, though she'd had to fill the role of both for the last eight years. And why? Because of that interfering old cow, Suzanne Palmer. If she'd been a man, he'd have flattened her.

"Are you staying for dinner?"

The question, he realized, had been aimed at him. By his daughter. The one he'd been denied all these years. She had a voice like music, like a creek cascading down a hillside. Like the wind in April. Sweet, reviving.

"Duh?" he replied, sounding more like a congenital idiot than a man in control of the situation.

Mona, good woman that she was, leaped to his rescue. "Well, of course they are, darling," she chuckled. "We're going to barbecue hamburgers, and I baked a rhubarb pie this afternoon. In a little while, when we've finished our tea, you can help me pick lettuce out of the garden, and we'll make a salad."

The gappy, winsome smile came into play again. "Can we eat outside at the picnic table and toast marshmallows, as well?"

"If our guests don't mind roughing it a bit."

Imogen picked up the conversational ball, tossing it smoothly back and forth. Just as well. About the only things he felt up to tossing were his cookies.

They were at it again, the women. Yammering on as they cleared the cups away and started hauling stuff out of the refrigerator. Meanwhile, his daughter unscrewed the top of a jar and chirped something about feeding the goldfish in the backyard pond.

Passing behind her, Imogen stroked a hand over Cassie's hair and said she wished her hair was curly like that. Cassie looked at her, the beginnings of hero worship lighting her eyes. He guessed it made sense. Imogen was pretty and young and stylish, exactly the kind of woman a little girl would look up to and admire, whereas he—what the hell had he to offer?

"What I'd really like is a horse," he heard his daughter say with an enchanting giggle. "But goldfish don't eat as much or take up as much room."

I could give you a horse, he wanted to tell her. *If things were as they ought to be, I could teach you to ride and buy you everything you need to become a first-rate equestrienne.*

Instead, he sat there tongue-tied and pretended he was just some guy who'd stopped in for dinner.

"Do you want to come and watch?" She addressed the question to the room at large, but she was standing near enough that he could have reached out and set her on his knee if he'd dared. She had long black eyelashes, tiny little ears that lay flat against the sides of her head and a dimple in each cheek.

He ached to hold her close, to smell the sweet skin scent of her after she'd had her bath, to have her skinny little arms wind around his neck as he piggybacked her upstairs to bed every night. Every night, damn it!

"I'd like to," Imogen told her, giving him a look that said, *For crying out loud, you dumb cluck, if you can't find something to say, at least have the good grace to shut your mouth and stop slobbering.* "I used to have a fish pond in the garden when I was a little girl."

Cassie skipped off, tugging Imogen along by the hand, while he continued to sit there like a maudlin sot who'd had one too many. To his horror, he found his eyes filling with tears. Jeez, what a time to make an ass of himself!

"You know, I could swear I bought another jar of mayonnaise, but I don't see it anywhere." Mona clicked her tongue in annoyance, but to Joe it was a heaven-sent opportunity to escape and try to get himself together.

Blinking furiously, he hauled himself out of the chair and said, "I'll drive down to the nearest store and pick one up for you."

"Not in my car you won't!" Imogen said, coming into the kitchen in time to hear his offer. "It's a rental and doesn't have your name on the contract. If it did, I'd tell you to start driving and keep going till you drop off the end of the earth."

"What the hell!" He moved back, affronted. "What have I done?"

"It's what you haven't done, you dolt!" She jerked her thumb at the open door and the garden beyond. "That's our daughter out there, itching to share her world with us. Is it asking too much for you to show a little interest?"

"I'm interested," he said, hanging on to his temper by a thread. Jeez, he felt ragged enough around the edges without Miss High and Mighty Palmer reading him the riot act!

"You could have fooled me!" she said, sneering. "The way you sat there gaping without a flicker of expression on your face had me wondering if you were brain-dead."

All the raw emotion rose to choke him. "Don't assume, just because I wasn't fawning all over her and babbling like you, that I—"

"How dare you, Joe Donnelly! I never babble!"

"Of course not. You never do anything wrong. It's always someone else's fault when things don't work out. That's the story of your life, princess. And what's ticking you off now is that you can't point the finger of

blame at me for the mess we've suddenly found ourselves in."

She looked about ready to smack him in the mouth
when Mona interrupted. "About that mayonnaise," she
said, reaching for a set of keys on a hook near the back
door. "You're welcome to take my car, Joe. And since
you're going out anyway, dear, would you mind picking
up another bag of marshmallows? Take your time and
have a look around town, if you like." She turned over
the keys to him with a knowing look and gave his hand
a surreptitious squeeze. "There's no hurry on dinner.
Now that school's out for the summer, I don't worry so
much about Cassie getting to bed on time."

"Thanks," he said, grateful for her intervention. He
couldn't remember when he'd last come so close to losing it.

He found the little shopping mall Mona had directed
him to easily enough. There was the usual collection of
small businesses—bakery, supermarket, drugstore, liquor outlet, barber and real estate office.

He hit the supermarket first, found the particular brand
of mayonnaise Mona had asked for and the marshmallows and was headed for the checkout when he passed
the candy shelf. Well, hell, he might not have grown up
in the rarefied atmosphere of Clifton Hill, but even a guy
from Lister's Meadows knew enough to buy a woman a
token of appreciation once in a while, and in his book,
he owed Mona Wyborn a lot more than a box of chocolates. But it was the best he could come up with on
such short notice—that and the bottle of champagne he
picked up in the liquor outlet, along with a six-pack of
beer.

He was on his way to the car when he noticed the ad
in the window of the real estate office.

Distress sale—25 acre horse farm with 8 stall barn,
2 extra outbuildings, 6 paddocks, 70x130 outdoor riding ring, plus house. Cross fenced with creek running
through. Property needs upgrading.

The photo accompanying it showed gently rolling land,
a stand of oaks casting long shadows and the corner of
a barn that looked as if a good wind would flatten it.

He stared at the photo for long minutes, wishing,
wanting. If things had been different, what might he
have done with such an opportunity?

"Things happen for a reason," his mother always
said, "and it's not up to us to question why. We just
have to have faith that God knows what He's doing."

"You want a miracle, you have to make it happen,"
Charlie Greenway had told him the day he'd driven him
from the prison on Ojo del Diablo and taken him to the
horse ranch in the middle of the island to serve out the
rest of his sentence. "Wait for someone else to do it,
and you'll still be waiting when you die."

It was after six. They had the picnic table set, the barbecue ready to go and the hamburger patties made, but
still there was no sign of Joe.

"I can't imagine what's keeping him," Imogen said,
for at least the fifth time. "Do you suppose he's lost?"

Mona didn't seem unduly concerned. "If he is, he can
always phone, lovey."

"Maybe he's taken me at my word and gone for good.
Again."

"Or perhaps he saw that you both need a little time
to adjust to...things." She nodded to where Cassie sat
on the swing hanging from a branch of the sturdy maple
at the bottom of the garden. "I thought you were rather

hard on him, Imogen. Meeting his daughter for the first time quite tore him up, I'd say.''

"Not Joe," Imogen said firmly. "I never met a man so able to contain his emotions.''

Mona busied herself folding paper napkins and tucking them under the cutlery to stop them blowing away in the breeze. "And you know him pretty well, do you, lovey?''

"Yes, although he doesn't think so.''

"You fancy yourself in love with him, do you?''

"I think I easily could be, if he'd let me get close enough. But he's so…private.''

"He strikes me as a very proud man, Imogen. And a very honorable man. You might have forgiven him for leaving you pregnant, but I doubt he's forgiven himself.''

"But it wasn't his fault that I was alone. That much I did manage to weasel out of him on the way here today. He came for me that summer, the way he'd promised he would. If my mother hadn't lied and told him I'd left town rather than have to see him again, we might have worked things out between us and be together today.''

"And then again, you might not. You were only a girl at the time and hadn't the foggiest idea of what marrying him would have entailed. He couldn't offer you the kind of life you were used to, and I doubt that he can even today. Do you think he doesn't know that, lovey, or that he doesn't see it as a barrier he can likely never overcome?''

"So what does that leave us with, Nanny? Separate lives and the only thing we share in common is a child we can never acknowledge? Do you really think I'm so shallow that I wouldn't make whatever sacrifice is necessary to be able, some day, to tell her that we're her parents?'' The tears she thought she had in check suddenly welled up again. ''It's not that I think we have the right to take her away from you, you know that. But she's my daughter, and I love her.'' Stifling a sob, she pressed a fist to her chest. ''She's in here, Nanny. In my heart. And there's room for him, too, if only he'd see it. And if the day comes when we can tell her who we really are—''

''It will come, Imogen. I've always known that, just as I know I have no right to try to keep her from you. When the time is right, she'll be with you.''

''Well, if that's so, don't you think that the very least we should be able to offer her is some semblance of normality? Isn't it bad enough that we've missed the first eight years of her life without then asking her to split the rest between a mother who lives in Vancouver and a father who lives heaven only knows where?''

''He lives here,'' Joe said from the screened kitchen door, sneaking up on her for the second time that day and eavesdropping on a conversation not intended for his ears.

''What are you saying?'' Imogen cried. ''You weren't even sure where this town was until this morning. And where have you been? I could have bought out a whole store in the time it took you to pick up a couple of items.''

''Well, I did buy a farm, as well,'' he said. ''Does that count?''

She stared at him uncomprehendingly. ''A *farm?*''

''Yup.''

''Why?''

''It was too good a deal to pass up.''

She shook her head to clear the cobweb of confusion

he was creating. "Have you lost your mind, Joe
Donnelly?"

"Nope."

Of all the times to play the strong, silent type! "And
what do you plan to do with it?" she snapped. "Or
doesn't your vocabulary extend to more than one-word
answers?"

"What do you think, princess?" he drawled infuriat-
ingly. "I'm going to work it."

"But you don't know anything about farming."

"That just goes to show how little you know about
me. Or else you never listen when other people are talking. Because I distinctly remember telling you that I
worked with horses out in California, and the place I
bought just happens to be a horse farm."

"I don't believe you! Where is this farm?"

"I don't know. I haven't seen it yet. Not far away
from here, though."

"Not seen it yet? Good grief, you *are* mad."

"Hey, cut me a little slack, will you?" he said, dump-
ing two bags on the picnic table. "By the time I made
some phone calls to the west coast and signed an interim
agreement of sale, it was after six, and you're already
bent out of shape because I took too long getting back."

How many more insults they might have traded had
Mona not stepped in was anyone's guess. After taking
the mayonnaise and marshmallows out of one bag, she
peered into the other. "Joe, is this champagne I see?"

His stony expression melted into a grin. "Yeah.
Already chilled, too. You want me to put it in the refrigerator, Mona, or shall we crack it open now?"

"I think now, dear. We seem to have rather a lot to
celebrate. While you do the honors, I'll see if I can find

us something suitable to drink out of. I'm afraid I don't have any real champagne glasses.''

"What on earth's gotten into you?" Imogen hissed the moment Mona disappeared inside the house.

"Fatherhood," he said, stripping away the foil collar on the bottle.

"That's no reason to rush out and invest in real estate on the spur of the moment. For heaven's sake, Joe, what were you thinking of?"

"My daughter. It's about time, wouldn't you say?"

She looked over her shoulder. The cat had come outside and Cassie, having abandoned the swing, had put him in her doll carriage and was busy covering him up with a blanket. "What are we going to do about her, Joe?"

"The only thing we can do. We're going to give her back her family. Why do you think I bought the farm?"

She stared at him, aghast. "You plan to take her away from Mona just like that?"

"No, Imogen. Tearing apart people's lives is your mother's specialty, not mine."

At that moment Mona came outside with three wineglasses. "I found chocolates in the kitchen, Joe. Did you get them for Cassie?"

"No. They're for you, Mona. Consider them a down payment on all I owe you."

He'd be charming the fruit off the apple tree next, Imogen thought sourly.

Loosening the wire securing it, he twisted the cork out of the bottle and poured the champagne. "I'd like to propose a toast," he said, handing the glasses around and raising his. "To the future."

"To the future," Mona responded, bright-eyed with optimism.

But Imogen was so busy trying to figure out what he was up to that she could barely choke down a mouthful of the wine. What had he meant when he'd said, "We're going to give her back her family"? More to the point, how did he plan to do so? "Joe, you and I need to talk," she said quietly.

"So you keep telling me," he said. "But right now, there are hamburgers waiting to go on the barbecue, and I'm the man to do the job."

He was avoiding having to face her, she realized eventually. Every time she tried to pry answers out of him, he found something else to keep himself occupied. First, it was flipping the hamburger patties over the charcoal, then it was refilling Mona's glass and chatting about tomato blight. But when he disappeared into the kitchen to get himself a beer, Imogen seized her chance. She cornered him between the refrigerator and the counter.

"All right, Joe Donnelly, I'm not going to stand idly by and let you play games with our daughter or Mona or me. I want to know what it is you think you're going to do, and I want to know now."

"I'm going to persuade Mona to leave this house and come to live on the farm," he said.

"Oh, honestly!" She shook her head in disgust. "Only you would think nothing of marching into someone else's life and just turning it upside-down without a thought for how it might affect the rest of the world. Even if you succeed in convincing Mona—"

"Oh, I'll succeed, princess," he assured her airily. "You, of all people, should know that once I make up my mind I want something, I don't back down until I've got it."

"And after you do, then what?"

"Then I'll tell Cassie that I'm her father and that she and her nanny are coming to live with me."

"And when she asks you where you were for the first eight years of her life, what are you going to tell her? Or are you so drunk on your own omnipotence that you haven't thought that far ahead?"

"Careful, Imogen. You're beginning to sound like your mother."

"Perhaps because I'm just discovering how it feels to be one," she said, knowing he was deliberately trying to antagonize her and refusing to rise to the bait. "Cassie is my child, too, remember. So where do I fit into this rosy picture you're painting, or have you decided I don't?"

"That's up to you. But to answer your other question, when Cassie asks me where I've been all this time, I intend to tell her the truth."

"Which is?"

"That it's taken me this long to grow up enough to deserve her, but now that I have, I don't ever intend letting her go again. What's your excuse going to be, princess?"

CHAPTER TEN

THE question plagued Imogen for the rest of the evening, overshadowing her pleasure in Cassie's company. She supposed she ate her hamburger like everyone else. Toasted the requisite number of marshmallows. Laughed in all the right places at the jokes. And yearned intolerably when, before she went to bed, Cassie came and leaned against her knee and said earnestly, "Will you still be here when I get up in the morning?"

But most of all, she raged inside at Joe. Oh, he was so sure he had all the answers! So much the man in charge, rushing out and buying property unseen, running errands, making decisions for other people without once stopping to question if he had the right! And such a coward when it came to facing his emotions. Did he think she hadn't noticed that he'd not once found an excuse to touch their child or engage her in private conversation?

When Cassie was in bed, he outlined his plans to Mona, wooing her with his smile, winning her over with his charm. These, added to the absolutely plausible way he proposed disrupting her entire life, were powerfully persuasive. "I'd never demand you give Cassie up or try to cut you out of her life, Mona, you know that. All I'm suggesting is that you share her with us. Am I asking too much?"

"Of course not," Mona said. "A child can never have too many people to love her, and you're her parents. She belongs with you."

"But she belongs with you, too. You've been her whole life so far, which is why I hope you'll agree to come and live on the farm with us. We need you, Mona, far more than you need us."

Us? Imogen thought furiously, feeling like a piece of furniture for all the notice he paid to what she might think. *Where's the us in all your grandiose plans? When did you last bother to consult me?*

"It's not much of a place right now," he confessed with a self-effacing little shrug and a cajoling tone, "but it will be when I'm finished with it. And the house is big, even if it is run-down. Over three thousand square feet. Room enough for all of us and close enough to the village that Cassie won't have to change schools."

Dazzled, Mona capitulated without a murmur, and in all fairness, Imogen could hardly blame her. Joe Donnelly in the role of new father out of his depth and floundering for want of a woman's support could, when he put his mind to it, move a stone idol to compassion. "I'm sure you'll do a wonderful job, dear, and you can count on me to help wherever I can."

He covered her work-worn hand with his. "I realize you've made a home here and that leaving it will be a wrench, but if it's for Cassie's sake…"

He angled another winsome smile her way and let the sentence hang, the blackmailing wretch!

Mona's eyes filled with tears of sympathetic understanding. "I would give my life for that child, Joe, don't you know that? This…" She looked at her chintz-covered furniture, her hoard of little treasures collected over a lifetime, then reached out her other hand to Imogen. "This is just a pile of bricks and lumber. We've been happy here, but home is where the heart is, so they say, and my heart will stay where it's always been—

with Cassie and her mother. If you can put up with having me underfoot all day, I'm not so old and set in my ways that I can't put up with a bit of a move.''

"Thank you!'' Pulling her to her feet, he wrapped her in a bear hug. "It'll take me the better part of the summer to make the place habitable but I'll have us settled in before school starts in September, I promise.''

"Right now,'' Imogen said, so ticked off at him that she was ready to spit, "I think we should let Mona get to bed. It's after ten, and we've got a three-hour drive in front of us.''

"Oh, didn't I tell you?'' he asked blithely. "We're staying here overnight. I've got papers to sign at the realtor's office first thing in the morning, and once that's taken care of, I thought we'd all take a run out to the farm and see just what it is I've bought, so I've booked us into a hotel in the village.''

"Without so much as a toothbrush?'' she asked indignantly. "Honestly, Joe Donnelly, did it ever occur to you I might have liked a little warning? Or is what *you* want and how *you* feel and what *you* think all that matters?''

"Quit fussing about nothing,'' he said, taking her elbow and steering her firmly toward the front door. "I'm sure the hotel can provide you with a toothbrush.''

"And a hairbrush and nightgown as well, no doubt!'' she wailed, yanking herself free. She knew she was making a fuss over trivialities, that compared to discovering her daughter was alive and well and accessible, being unprepared to spend the night in a hotel was nothing more than a minor blip in the cosmic scheme of things. But so help her, if he didn't wipe that condescending smile off his face...

Mona pursed her lips and cocked her head. "I'd offer

to put you up here, but it's perhaps as well that I don't have the room. The two of you need to sit down and talk things out in private. And, lovey, I can lend you what you need for the night, so don't fret about a little thing like that.''

He'd reserved adjoining rooms at the Norbury, a quaint old inn situated just above a waterfall on the river that ran through the village. She'd barely climbed out of the bath and into the voluminous nightgown Mona had found for her before he rapped on the connecting door.

''I've brought us a nightcap,'' he said, when she opened it. ''I thought we could use one.''

Uninvited, he marched into her room with two brandy snifters and parked himself in the armchair drawn up beside the tiny fireplace.

''And what if I don't want one?'' she snapped.

He pinned her with a weary gaze. ''Stop acting like a spoiled brat, Imogen, and drink the goddamned brandy. We need to fine-tune a few details.''

''I suppose I should be flattered you've finally seen fit to include me in your schemes,'' she said, flouncing to the bed and sitting cross-legged in the middle of the mattress with the nightgown tucked securely around her feet.

''Uh-oh.'' He contemplated his brandy, holding it to the firelight so it glowed in the glass like burning amber. ''What, specifically, have I done that has you puckering up as if you accidentally bit into a lemon?''

''I think you had an obligation to invite my opinion before you rushed out and bought a farm, sight unseen, with a view to coercing Mona and Cassie into living there with you. I don't appreciate being left out of decisions that materially affect my daughter's future.''

"The way you left me out when you decided to keep the news of your pregnancy to yourself, you mean? Or the way your mother left both of us out when she decided it was best for everybody to believe the baby had died?"

"Is that what this is all about, Joe? Getting even? Because if it is, let me tell you—"

"It isn't," he said flatly. "But one thing I can promise you is that I'll never again allow your mother to stick her interfering nose in my daughter's welfare. From now on, the dragon lady will have to go through me before she so much as drops Cassie a postcard."

"And where do I fit into the equation—or don't I?"

"Of course you do, Imogen. You're the other half of the two-parent package deal I'm offering Cassie. That being so, you and I are, to use one of your phrases, going to have to get married."

Even though she'd expressed more or less the same thought to Mona earlier, she was taken aback to hear it from him. "Who are you trying to impress, Joe? You're no more interested in marrying me than I am in having you for a husband."

"Oh, really? And are you willing to tell our daughter that she's finally found her real mother and father but since they never bothered getting married and are too self-absorbed to place her interests ahead of their own, she'll have to make do with living with her father and seeing her mother only occasionally?"

Imogen sprang up on the bed, rage and a terrible fear coursing through her. "Forget it, Joe Donnelly! I won't let you or anyone else separate me from my child ever again."

"And neither will I," he said implacably. "So let's set a date to tie the knot, princess."

*   *   *

She did not see him at all during the ten days prior to the wedding. The morning after their stay at the inn, Joe completed all the legal work entailed in the purchase of the farm. Then, as promised, he took her, Cassie and Mona to see the property and with a sensitivity that touched Imogen despite herself, introduced their daughter to the idea of the four of them living together.

"This is it," he said, interrupting his discourse on the pleasures of country living and pulling up in a gravel parking area at the end of a rutted, tree-lined lane. "Why don't you go and explore, then tell us what you think of the place?"

Cassie didn't wait to be asked twice. With a squeal of exuberant glee, she raced through the long grass of the nearest paddock like a young deer.

"I'll keep an eye on her while the two of you have a look around inside the house," Mona offered, climbing out of the car.

The silence she left behind hung in the air, as oppressive as a storm about to break. His lighthearted optimism dissipating, Joe leaned forward, crossed his forearms on the steering wheel and stared through the windshield.

His sigh told Imogen what he saw—the swaybacked roof of one of the outbuildings, the weeds choking the vegetable garden, the gate hanging off its hinges at the entrance to the nearest paddock, the paint peeling off the side of the house.

"Well, this is it, princess," he finally said. "Butternut Farm. Not quite what you're used to, I'm afraid, but it's the best I can do for now."

She was aware that he was waiting for her to throw up her hands in horror and declare she couldn't possibly make do with such a dump. But her vision was not his, and she could not speak. She was too entranced by the house and the way it sat on a little rise so that, morning and evening, its rooms would be flooded with sunshine.

Square-paned casement windows flanked a central front entrance accessed by a flight of steps. Four tall chimneys rose from the gabled roof. A covered porch ran around three walls of the building, with a purple clematis climbing one of the corner posts and clinging to the gingerbread fretwork below the gutters.

Old and neglected it might be, but this was a house whose timeless beauty relied less on cosmetic care than classic elegance of design. Long and low, it flowed into the landscape as if, like the old-fashioned rambling rose running riot along the picket fence, it, too, had sprung from deep and enduring roots.

"If you think your sitting there gaping is going to work some sort of miracle, be my guest," Joe said tersely, swinging open the driver's door and climbing out of the car, "but I'm going to check out the stables. If you're interested in seeing where you're going to be living, here are the keys to the house."

Imogen wasted no time embarking on her tour of inspection. The inside of the house bore out the promise of the exterior. She discovered oak floors, ten-foot ceilings, crown molding, wood-burning fireplaces, marvelous built-in, glass-fronted china cabinets in the dining room and a huge claw-footed cast-iron tub in the main upstairs bathroom.

Oh, she could make a home from such treasures! A place a man would be glad to return to at the end of a long, hard day. A place a little girl could learn to love.

Never mind the layer of dust covering everything, the wallpaper hanging off the dining room wall, the water stain on the ceiling of the master bedroom. They were surface flaws, easily remedied.

It didn't take much on the drive to Norbury to convince Cassie that living on a farm was the best idea in the world, especially not with Mona voicing her relief at having other people around to help her out when her arthritis acted up. "Because you know how my hips and knees bother me in the winter, Cassie," she said, adding as a final inducement, "and I daresay you'll be allowed to have that puppy you've always wanted because there's plenty of space for a dog to run around."

"Or even two," Joe said. "And, of course, there'll be horses, as well." The smile he turned on his daughter would have melted the polar ice cap. "You *are* still interested in having your own pony, aren't you?"

"That was nothing short of blatant bribery!" Imogen accused him, after they'd dropped Mona and Cassie at home and were on their way to Rosemont. "Cassie was so excited by your blandishments, she'd have agreed to live with the devil himself if you'd asked her."

"Let's hope she'll be content to settle for a mother and father when she learns they're also part of the deal," he said. "I don't know why you refused to lay it all out for her and have done with. What you do hope to gain by putting off the truth?"

"Time to win her love and trust." She chanced another look at him. "And time for us to ease into this marriage we're contemplating."

That night, she told her mother her plans, knowing that, across town in Lister's Meadows, Joe was telling his family all that had transpired in the last two days.

"That man my son-in-law?" Suzanne gasped. "Dear heaven, I pray he isn't planning to call me 'mother'!"

The next morning, Imogen flew to Vancouver to close

up her apartment and clean out her office. "It seems awfully sudden," the firm's senior partner joked when she said she was leaving to get married. "How do you know this man deserves you?"

But once she'd heard the whole story and had recovered from the shock of learning that Cassie was alive, Tanya hadn't been able to keep the smirk off her face. "See what a good friend I am, pushing you into going home?" she crowed delightedly. "I always believed there was unfinished business between you and Joe and, oh brother, was I right! Everything's going to work out for you now, you'll see."

Imogen wished she shared her friend's optimism. But to her, the future looked anything but certain. The miracle of finding her daughter alive was counterbalanced by a marriage made anywhere but in heaven.

"So what if ours isn't the ideal arrangement?" Joe had argued, when she pointed out that they weren't in love. "We're not doing this for us, we're doing it for Cassie, which means that, from the day we all start living under one roof, we're going to present an unblemished portrait of wedded bliss and family unity, right down to apple pie on Sundays and Mom and Dad reading bedtime stories."

"What if we can't?"

"We will," he said flatly. "And I fail to see why you should even doubt it, given that you've been keeping up appearances from the day you were born. So get used to the idea, princess, because although I can't make up for what she's missed so far, I'll move heaven and earth to make sure Cassie never again has reason to question why her life is different from other kids'."

"And how far are you prepared to go with this charade?" Imogen had retorted, when what she really wanted to know was how he planned to behave toward her in private. Did the semblance of one big happy family end when they were alone, or was he prepared to be as devoted a husband as he was a father?

"Right down to the wire, princess," he said. "So if you're asking if we'll be sharing a bedroom, yes, we will. That's the way parents live, in case you hadn't noticed. But if you're worrying I'm going to demand my husbandly rights behind closed doors, don't. If it weren't for my boss in California helping me out, I'd never have been able to afford the farm. As it is, I've mortgaged my soul to buy the place, and it's going to take long days of hard labor to make it turn a profit. I don't anticipate having the energy to romp around in bed every night."

An icy fist had seemed to close around her heart at that. When she was eighteen, the thought of being married to Joe Donnelly would have enthralled her. At twenty-three, he'd been carefree and excitingly dangerous. Now, he was just dangerous. There was a cold determination in him that amounted almost to anger. He would not rush out, a knight on a Harley, to save a damsel in distress—unless she happened to be his daughter. And for Cassie, he'd made it plain enough, he would sacrifice anyone, including the woman he married.

Once her affairs were settled in Vancouver, she hitched a trailer of possessions to her car and drove across the country to Ontario, arriving at the farm the evening before the wedding. The California license plates on the pickup truck outside the barn told her Joe already was there.

"For crying out loud, Imogen," he said, coming upon

her lugging one of her trunks through the front door, "why didn't you get me to carry that in?"

No, "Hi, honey, glad you made the trip safely." No embrace. She supposed she should be glad he offered to help her unload the trailer.

"Where do you want me to put this?" he asked, bringing in the last of the crates as she carried in her suitcases.

"Upstairs," she panted, blowing a wisp of hair from her damp forehead. It was a typical July night in Ontario, hot and humid. She'd been on the road for four days, she was ready to drop from exhaustion and nervous tension, and tomorrow was her wedding day.

More than anything she would have liked to take a long, cool bath, give herself a manicure, then slip into a robe and spend a quiet evening sharing a bottle of wine and a few dreams with her fiancé. But Joe had other ideas.

"I had cleaners in while you were gone," he said, "and bought new kitchen appliances, but I'm waiting for the electrician to finish rewiring before I can get the kitchen up and running. He's promised he'll stop by on his way home so, since there's not much more that can be done tonight, you might as well drive into the village and hit the sack. I booked you into the Norbury for the next few days."

She'd noticed the sleeping bag on the floor in the master bedroom and the clothes hanging in the closet. "I gather you've been staying here?"

"Uh-huh. I'm here working all day, anyway."

"I can see that." The roof on the house and the big barn had been replaced and sections of broken fence repaired. Whatever his faults, Joe wasn't afraid of hard work. "But wouldn't you be more comfortable sleeping in the hotel?"

He shrugged. "I don't mind the floor. I've slept on worse, and at least this is clean and dry. I'd have bought some furniture but I thought you'd probably prefer to choose it yourself, though I warn you now, Imogen, I don't have much cash to spare."

"I do," she said, daring to broach a subject they'd discussed only once, the night he'd taken her to dinner. "I know how you feel about accepting financial help from a woman, but there's no reason we have to scrimp and save on turning this house into a home. In fact, there's no reason you have to carry a mortgage on the property. Once we're married, what's mine is yours, and you'll be able to pay off the loan and still have money in the bank."

She hadn't expected him to leap at her offer. Even so, she was taken aback by the vehemence of his rejection. "Don't even start on that theme!" he raged. "It'll be a cold day in hell before I use Palmer money to meet the bills. I might not have much by your standards, but at least I have my pride, and I'm damned if I'm going to let you strip me of it."

"What are you talking about?" she cried. "I thought we were in this together, that we were trying to make a good home for our daughter, and plenty of couples need a double income to live on these days. Why can't I do my part?"

"You can," he said sullenly. "You just can't buy it."

She sighed, her weariness as much of the heart and soul as of the body, and headed for the front door. "That's not what I'm doing, and if you really want this marriage to hold together, you're going to have to get rid of that monumental chip on your shoulder. I'm not the enemy here, Joe, and if I'm willing to trust your motivation, the least you can do is return the favor and show a little faith in mine.''

She was almost at her car when he came out of the house and called after her. ''Wait a minute!''

She watched warily as he loped down the porch steps. ''You're right,'' he said, coming to a stop beside her. ''At least, on this matter of trust. So, for what it's worth, I don't think you're trying to buy your place in this marriage. But please understand that making the money end of it work has to be my responsibility.''

They were married in a civil ceremony at nine-thirty the next morning. There was no confetti, no champagne, no idyllic honeymoon suite in one of the many charming inns on the Niagara peninsula that catered to newlyweds. Nor were there any guests. Two strangers acted as witnesses.

Imogen did not wear white or carry a bouquet. She made do with a simple cotton shift dress the color of ripe wheat. It was more than sufficient, given that the groom showed up in blue jeans. And when the officiating clerk pronounced them husband and wife, Joe did not sweep her into a crushing embrace and tell her he loved her. Instead, before the plain gold wedding ring had had time to warm up on her finger, he said, ''I'm meeting a contractor at the house in an hour. Let's get going.''

''Do you mind driving my car and leaving the truck with me? There are a few errands I have to run,'' she said.

He barely spared her a glance and expressed not a word of curiosity about where she was going or why, simply tossed her his keys and took hers. "See you at the farm later on then," he said.

It was close to two o'clock when she returned. Joe was working in the stable. Poking her head in the door, she called, "Thought you might be ready for lunch, so I picked up sandwiches and something cold to drink."

"Leave them in the truck and I'll take a break when I'm done with this," he said, not bothering to lift his head from the task at hand.

She shrugged. After unloading all the various supplies she'd bought, she ate a sandwich as she wandered from room to room in the house and decided which job she'd tackle first.

The sun hung low in the western sky when he finally put in an appearance. She was perched on a stepladder propped somewhat precariously against the banister, painting the stairwell walls and ceiling a soft oyster white. "What the hell do you think you're doing, Imogen?" he demanded, stopping just inside the front door.

"What does it look like?" she asked, swiping the back of her hand over her forehead. "I'm brightening up the house."

He came to the foot of the stairs and stared at her. She wished he wouldn't. She'd changed into a pair of bibbed shorts and a T-shirt and was very aware that, from his vantage point, all he could see were her legs.

"Get down from that ladder right now," he said.

"In a minute. I'm not quite finished."

He swore rather colorfully. "What's your hurry, for Pete's sake? Mona and Cassie aren't moving in for another five weeks, and you're comfortable enough at the inn. You don't have to put everything in apple-pie order in one day."

"I moved out of the inn," she said, stretching on tip-toe to reach the last corner.

"What the hell for?"

"Because it's an expense we can do without. And we are married now, Joe, so there's no great sin attached to my living with my husband, is there? Furthermore," she continued, when all he did was grunt, "I like to keep busy, and since this is going to be my home as well as yours, I intend to do my share in making it livable."

"Not like this," he said. "It's not your sort of work."

"Oh, really?" She paused to concentrate on one last touch to the wall. "And exactly what *is* my sort of work?"

"I don't know. Making lists, I suppose. Isn't that what women like you do best?"

"Among other things," she said, and leaned back to admire her handiwork, a movement that caused the stepladder to tilt alarmingly.

"Jeez!" He surged up the stairs to steady it, then grabbed her around the hips and hauled her down to the landing. "You aren't going to be much use at all in a body cast, you know!"

His eyes shot fire, and his breathing was rapid and furious. She didn't care. They were standing hip to hip, knee to knee, and she could feel his heart racing under her hand, feel the warmth of his skin. With only the smallest of movements she could have reached up and tasted his mouth. She had not been so close to him since the night they'd walked by the river and he'd almost forgotten himself so far as to make love to her.

"Do you realize," she said softly, tracking his features one by one and wishing she could find them merely ordinary instead of unforgettably beautiful, "that this is the first time you've held me since I became your wife?"

A faint flush ran over his cheekbones, and he slid his gaze away so that all she could see were the twin fans of his lashes shielding the deep cobalt irises. "Don't do this, Imogen. We've got enough to deal with over the next few weeks without any added complications."

"Is that all I am to you, Joe?" she whispered, cupping his jaw tenderly. "A complication? A necessary evil?"

He thrust her away from him. "Stop it, I said! You're all ready to take this marriage by storm and damn the consequences, but let's see how eager you are a month from now, when the novelty of waving a paintbrush around has worn off and the man you married is gone from dawn to dusk every day, seven days a week, trying to whip this farm into shape before winter. There won't be any posh soirees to relieve the tedium, princess. No elegant parties, no dinner dances at the club."

"I came into this marriage with my eyes wide-open," she said, stung by his certainty that she'd fold under pressure. "The very least you can do is give me the chance to show you what I'm made of before you decide I'm not up to the job I've taken on."

A spark of humor lightened his eyes. "I already know what you're made of, Imogen. That's half the trouble."

"Well, learn to live with it," she snapped, pulling away. "Because you're just as stuck with me as I am with you. And while I'm speaking my mind, here's something else you can chew on. You've done nothing but lay down the law from the minute you learned Cassie was alive. Well, I was just as much deceived as you were, and I'm not about to let you make me pay for my mother's sins. If it's a whipping boy you're looking for, find one somewhere else."

"I never—"

She cut him off in mid-splutter. "I'm not the shel-

tered, submissive little girl you rescued nine years ago,
Joe Donnelly. Somewhere along the line, I grew up and
came to grips with the real world. I can paint. I can hang
wallpaper. I can sew curtains and do any of a hundred
other things to turn a house into a home. I have a list of
satisfied clients willing to attest to that. So I'll make you
a deal. You do what you have to to bring the farming
end of this partnership up to scratch, and leave me to
take care of what I have to do. I won't tell you how to
do your job as long as you don't tell me how to do
mine." She fixed him with a determined stare. "Well?
What's it to be?"

He didn't like it, not one bit, but he had to live with it.
Because she was right. The house left a lot to be desired,
and the last thing he wanted was for Cassie to be unhappy there.

Actually, that wasn't quite the last thing he wanted.
He wanted Imogen. His wife. The woman who, over the
next two weeks, got up at dawn and made him breakfast
and had dinner waiting for him when he dragged himself
to the house after sunset. And who, every night until the
decorating was done, came to sleep on the floor next to
him, smelling of flowers from her bath and wearing a
modest cotton nightdress that hung to her ankles.

She never once complained at roughing it. He wished
she would. Then he could have suggested they buy a
bed big enough to hold both of them. But apart from
that night when he'd been certain she was going to fall
off the stepladder and topple headfirst down the stairs,
she'd not so much as hinted at any sort of intimacy between them.

Instead, she painted and hung wallpaper, polished
floors and windows. And he discovered that when she

was absorbed in a task, she tended to run the tip of her tongue slowly over her upper lip. He wondered what she'd say if he told her how erotic he found the habit.

To keep cool while she was working, she wore paint-spattered shorts. To keep cool, he tried not to stare at her legs. Her nails, which had been long and painted pink the day she married him, were trimmed short, and he berated himself in mindless fury because he couldn't keep her in the fashion to which she'd been accustomed all her life.

Then, one day when the heat had been particularly unbearable, he came home to find she'd cut her hair. Instead of lying nearly to her shoulders, it just cleared her jaw. It made her look eighteen again and set him to wishing for impossible things, like turning the clock back and starting over with her from scratch, with orange blossom and lace and all those other things young women hoped for when they got married.

Gradually, her ideas and efforts began to transform what he'd seen as a barren shell of a house into a place of charm and warmth. Yet despite the hours she put in, she somehow found time to visit Cassie and Mona or invite them to drop by the farm and see how things were progressing.

He'd come in for lunch and find a picnic set up on the covered porch, the three of them waiting for him to join them. Cassie would be full of questions about how he trained a horse and when he was going to teach her to ride and what sort of puppy they'd be getting. The shyness that had kept them at a distance from each other slowly melted away until the day came when she leaped off the porch and came running to meet him, and he caught her in his arms in a hug, and she clung to him like a limpet.

He thought he'd never forget the feel of her skinny little arms wrapped so tight around his neck that she almost choked him. He had to pretend he had dust in his eye to hide the fact that he could hardly see for the tears that blinded him.

Toward the end of the third week, he came home to find a load of furniture had been delivered, along with half a dozen packing crates. When he accused her of dipping into her own funds, Imogen assured him she'd stayed within his budget and used only the money he'd left for her.

"Haunting estate sales, flea markets and antique fairs was part of my job in Vancouver," she said offhandedly when he asked her how that was possible. "If a person knows what to look for, there are some excellent bargains to be had."

"Well, don't try moving any of this heavy stuff yourself," he told her. "I'll knock off an hour or two early and lend a hand before dinner."

So while she filled the built-in cabinets in the dining room with some turn-of-the-century bride's wedding china, he arranged eight matching chairs around a long oak table and rewired an old brass chandelier she'd unearthed from the cellar.

After she'd laid a thick white rug on the living room floor, he hauled in a dark green velvet couch and set it in front of the fireplace. She took an old kitchen dresser the previous owners had left behind, and which he'd have thrown on a bonfire, and stripped it down to bare wood, then waxed it to a soft shine and filled the shelves with blue and white pottery she'd brought from the west coast. Meanwhile, he built new shelves for every closet in the house.

But there were empty spots in every room, too, "for

Mona to put her things," she told him, "because we don't want her to feel she's lost her home. And, of course, I haven't furnished Cassie's bedroom. I'll let her choose how she'd like it to be."

"I have to go away for a few days," he told her at the end of the first week in August. "There's a horse auction I want to attend in New Jersey."

He'd thought of asking her to come with him, even gone so far as to wonder if they couldn't turn the trip into a sort of honeymoon. But she scotched that idea before it had even hatched.

"Then go, and don't worry about me. I've got plenty to keep me busy here."

Enough that she wouldn't notice he was gone? he wondered.

He came home a week later, driving from first light until nearly midnight because, damn it, he missed her so much he could practically taste it. By the time he'd settled his four new horses in the stable, it was almost one o'clock, one of those perfect August nights where the moon hung like a great silver ball and a million stars dotted the sky.

He stood on the porch outside the front door and looked over the land, at the fences he'd repaired gleaming pale in the moonlight and the still black shape of the butternut trees for which the farm was named and the newly painted stables and barns.

It was more than he'd ever thought to own, and all because of a child who still did not know he was her father. And a wife he never kissed.

The house was dark and silent behind him, and he did not want to waken her, but he was dusty from his journey and smelled of horses and needed a bath. The best he could do was fill a pail from the rain barrel at the back door, scrub down there, then rinse himself off. The water was warm from the sun and rolled off him like silk, sluicing over his shoulders and through his hair.

Dripping, he let himself inside the house. The moon shone through the high window on the landing, casting his shadow ahead of him, long and ungainly. He found a towel in the bathroom, mopped himself dry, brushed his teeth. And like a child saving the best part of the cake for last, finally made his way to the bedroom.

There was a bed against the far wall. A huge brass-railed affair with her asleep in the middle of it. On another wall was a tall chest of drawers and in the corner a mirror on a stand.

He edged his way around a cedar chest at the foot of the bed and waited until he'd shut himself in the walk-in closet before he turned on the light. He blinked at the sight that met his eyes.

Some eager beaver had been at work. Half the space was filled with women's things made of soft, feminine fabrics. And the other half... The jeans and work shirts he'd piled on the floor had been neatly arranged on hangers with his belts dangling next to them from some gadget screwed into the wall. But the undershorts and socks he'd shoved on one of the shoe shelves on the end wall—they were gone!

Well, hell! He supposed she'd moved them into the chest of drawers in the bedroom. Feeling ridiculous, he turned off the light, let himself out of the closet and retraced his steps across the bedroom, thankful that at least there was enough moonlight that he didn't fall over his own feet.

Carefully, he inched open the top drawer of the dresser and felt around at the contents. They were definitely not undershorts—he wasn't into satin. He drew a blank in the second drawer, too, and was bent over the third when she woke up to the realization there was an intruder going through her things.

Her scream split the night in two. And did he disabuse her of the fact that he wasn't some kinky burglar bent on stealing her underthings and try to calm her fears? Not fearless Joe Donnelly! He clapped one hand over his private parts and tried to run out of the room before she saw all he had to offer.

She caught him a glancing blow on the shoulder with a book, hurled with more energy than accuracy, thank God, because it weighed about five pounds. "For Christ's sake, princess!" he yelped, ducking as the alarm clock winged past. "It's only me. Hold your fire!"

CHAPTER ELEVEN

"JOE?" She uttered his name on a quaking breath of terror, and without thinking he turned to reassure her. As he did, she switched on the bedside lamp.

She sat in the middle of the bed like a china doll, her blue eyes wide as they roamed the length and breadth of him. He spun so that his back was to her and spoke over his shoulder. "Sorry if I woke you. I was just looking for some—"

"Underwear?" Her voice was laced with laughter, and he realized she was watching him in the mirror and could see everything he'd gone to such absurd lengths to hide. "You'll find it over there, in the chifforobe."

Chifforobe? Wildly, he looked around to identify what the hell she was talking about and discovered a handsome combination wardrobe and chest of drawers hidden behind the open bedroom door. He snatched a pair of shorts from the top drawer and hurriedly climbed into them. Then, and only then, did he look her in the face.

She'd moved to the right side of the mattress, leaving the other half empty. "I guess we should get some sleep," he said, feeling like the biggest damned fool ever to walk the face of the earth. "The sun'll be up in another four hours, and I've got horses to tend to."

"You found what you were looking for?" Her smile put the stars to shame. "That's wonderful!"

"If I'd had a bigger trailer, I'd have bought more," he said, reaching over to switch off the lamp before slid-

174

ing into bed next to her. "There was a stallion I wish I could have brought back for stud."

The bed smelled of her, all flowery and fresh, and no sooner had he drawn the top sheet over his waist than she slithered across the space between them. "I'd really like to get started on a breeding program," he said, lying very still.

She snuggled closer. "I'm so glad you're home again, Joe."

"For horses," he said, his voice a croak.

"I've missed you," she whispered, her breath sweet against his neck.

The defenses he'd struggled to maintain crumbled. "Oh, hell, Imogen," he groaned, pulling her hard against him, "I've missed you, too. I sometimes think I've missed you all my life."

"You have every right," she said. "You're my husband."

He couldn't help himself for what he did next, because it was something he'd wanted for longer than he cared to remember. He kissed her, knowing that, this time, he wouldn't stop at that. She tasted of passion, dark and erotic, of desire simmering beneath the surface of her cream-smooth skin.

For a little while, he was content to hold her and to feel the cold uncertainty that had dogged him since he'd rushed out and bought the farm, just to show her he was able to give her and their daughter a home, began to melt. Too soon, though, holding her wasn't enough. It never had been, not with her. He wanted all of her, everything she was willing to give.

Slowly he raised her nightgown until she lay naked and quivering beside him. She let him touch her, let him feast his eyes on her breasts and belly, all silvered in the moonlight. Let him kiss her in places she'd never been kissed before, not even by him. And when he heard her cry out his name and convulse against him, he thought he was the world's biggest fool to have waited six weeks to make her his wife in every sense of the word.

He kicked off the underwear he'd been so anxious to put on and poised himself above her, not quite touching his flesh to hers. Teasing her and tormenting himself almost beyond human endurance. Then, when her frantic urgings became more than he could withstand and he thought he would burst from wanting her, he said hoarsely, "I love you, princess," and buried himself in her warm, dark depths.

With embarrassing speed, the quiet night exploded, shattering them both. He melted within her, helpless to protect either of them from the raging wildfire. All he could do was hold her and murmur over and over, "I love you." Because it was true.

She clung to him sobbing, her body racked by a soft and lovely keening of fulfilment that echoed the fading spasms that had gripped it moments before. And gradually, the heat cooled to a warm afterglow, and he found the strength to wrap them both in the sheet and wipe the tears from her face with fingers not designed for so delicate a task.

She made him feel big and clumsy. She made him feel like a king.

He had already left when she awoke the next morning. Stealing to the window, she looked out and saw him in the top paddock with four young horses, two chestnut, one roan and one black. He sat perched on the fence, watching them as they explored their new home.

When he let himself in the back door an hour later,

she was at the kitchen stove making scrambled eggs and hardly knew how to look at him. Did he regret the night they'd shared? Had he meant the words he'd repeated so desperately in the throes of passion?

She did not wonder for long. Coming up behind her, he wrapped his arms around her waist, then slid his palms up to cover her breasts. "Morning, Mrs. Donnelly," he said against her neck, and turned her to find her mouth.

How was it possible that he could so deftly turn her molten with hunger with just a word, a touch? Her lips were tender from the night before, and she ached all over from his lovemaking, yet her body clamored for him again. As did his for her. The thrust of his hips left her in little doubt of that.

"Are you hungry?" she asked, struggling to contain herself.

"Starving," he murmured, and reaching behind her, turned off the stove and steered her to where four high stools stood next to the breakfast bar.

Deliberately, he inched down her shorts and found the sleek, damp nub of flesh awaiting him. More hurriedly, he unzipped his jeans and cupped her bottom in his hands.

At the other end of the counter, the coffeemaker burbled and splashed hot liquid into its carafe. His breath rasped urgently against her mouth. She clung to him and wound her legs around his waist, dizzy with hunger.

The bread she'd put in the toaster popped up with a metallic ping. Simultaneously, he plunged into her. Again and again. Time after time, until she disintegrated and sank against him, limp and satiated.

And then the phone rang.

A laugh rolled through him, rumbling like an earth-

quake and shaking them both. He reached out one long
arm, lifted the receiver and propped it in the angle of
his shoulder. "Butternut Farm," he said, as if butter
wouldn't melt in his mouth.

A voice came faintly over the line, and another quiver
of laughter shook him. "She's right here, Mrs. Palmer,"
he said. "Hold on."

Oh, he was every bit as bad as rumor had always
painted him! Worse, in fact! All the time she tried to
hold an intelligent conversation with her mother, he nib-
bled at her neck, her ears, the corner of her mouth. When
she tried to slide to the floor, he imprisoned himself
more firmly inside her and rocked against her.

"Hurry up," he murmured. "The eggs are growing
cold."

Overhearing, her mother inquired, "Am I keeping you
from breakfast, dear?"

"Yes," Imogen said breathlessly, feeling the treacherous tide rise up and begin to overtake her again. "We
were just about to get started. May I call you back a
little later?"

"So what," he asked, as they sat with their coffee in
the newly painted wicker chairs on the east porch, "did
Mother want?"

"To drive down to see Cassie." She shot him a look
from beneath her lashes. "I suggested she meet her here.
I hope you don't mind."

He stared across the gently rolling landscape and
chewed his lip reflectively. After a while, he sighed and
said, "I guess that brings us smack up against the one
thing we haven't yet resolved, princess."

"Yes." Suddenly afraid, she put her cup on the table

and wiped damp hands on her napkin. "How we're going to tell Cassie the truth."

He saw her distress. Leaning forward, he took her hands and covered them with his. "We'll find a way, sweetheart. And if, when she finds out who we are, she finds it too much to handle, we'll keep trying until we make her understand. But regardless of the outcome, I won't let it come between you and me."

"But what if it does anyway, Joe? You never really wanted to get married and especially not to me. What if you find you did it all for nothing and she won't accept you as her father?"

"Listen to me, Imogen," he said firmly. "When I first learned there'd been a baby and I hadn't known about it, I was angry and looking for someone to blame. And since you were standing right in the line of fire, I blamed you. But I was aiming at the wrong person. Yes, your mother was wrong to lie, to deprive you of your child, and maybe you shouldn't have let her take charge like that. But the real fault lies with me, and I'm sorry it's taken me so long to admit it."

"How is it your fault?" she asked, her throat thick with tears.

"If I'd stood by you, sweetheart, none of the rest would have happened. I should never have left you to face your mother alone, never allowed her to run me off the property when I came looking for you. It's easy to make excuses, but the bottom line is, I let myself be dissuaded from keeping in touch with you because I wasn't ready for a serious relationship. At least, I thought I wasn't. I had no way of knowing how often, in the years that followed, I'd think of you and wonder if I threw away a gem without realizing it. I know now that I did."

"Don't make my cry," she said, laughing at the tears sliding down her face. "My mother will think you beat me if she gets here and my eyes are all red."

"I'd like to kiss you," he said, "but knowing what a nymphomaniac I married, I'm afraid to. Bad enough your mother listened in to me making love to you without her taking pictures, as well."

She dissolved into giggles. "Oh, Joe, I do love you," she said.

He leaned over and kissed her anyway. "Good. Because you're stuck with me."

Quite a crowd showed up that afternoon. At Imogen's suggestion, Joe phoned his parents and invited them, too. "I guess you're right," he said. "It's time we introduced Cassie to her other grandparents. As it is, I don't know how my mother's contained herself this long."

Mona and Cassie arrived first, with a box of home-baked cookies and a lemon chiffon cake. "And a few small items from the house," Mona explained, opening the trunk of her car. "I thought we might as well start packing things up, since we'll be moving out here for good in another week or two."

Suzanne and the Donnellys showed up within five minutes of each other, about an hour later, and met on the south porch, where Imogen had grouped the wicker chairs around a table set with glasses and a pitcher of iced tea.

Suzanne offered a gloved hand to Mrs. Donnelly. "How do you do? I understand we're more or less related."

"Rather more than less, if you ask me," Mrs. Donnelly said, her gaze fixing itself hungrily on Cassie, who was in her element playing maid and handing out plates and linen tea napkins.

Joe caught up with Imogen in the kitchen when she went inside to replenish the iced tea. "Talk about being able to cut the air with a knife," he muttered. "The tension out there is enough to stop a moose in its tracks."

"I thought everyone seemed to be getting along fine," she said, putting cookies on a plate.

"Are you kidding?"

"Well, they're not at each other's throats."

"Perhaps not, but your mother's parked on her chair like the queen of Sheba on her throne, making small talk about the weather, and my dad's practically having to sit on my mom to stop her from grabbing Cassie and smothering her in kisses. What if Cassie can't cope with so much all at once, princess? What do we do then?"

"I don't know," Imogen said, her confidence waning in the face of his doubt.

But in the end, Suzanne saved the day, and in doing so redeemed herself a little for the terrible deception she'd practiced for so many years. "I think," she announced regally, "that since we're all aware of certain…undercurrents for which I am largely responsible, perhaps I should be the one to put an end to them. Cassandra, my dear, come and sit beside me and let me tell you a story you should have heard a long time ago. Once upon a time, there was a very pretty young girl."

"Was she a princess?" Cassie asked.

"Yes," Joe said. "She was my princess."

"Quite," Suzanne said, slipping Cassie onto her lap and giving him a quelling look. "But her mother was rather a wicked queen, I'm afraid, and she decided that the young man who wanted to marry her daughter and take her away on his, er, black horse—''

''What was the horse's name?'' Cassie wanted to know.

''Harley,'' Joe said irrepressibly, while Imogen sat with her fists clenched against her heart to keep it from leaping clean out of her chest. ''Harley-Davidson.''

Suzanne cleared her throat imperiously. ''As I was saying, the queen decided that the princess was much too young to look after the little girl she gave birth to one winter's morning. So she took the baby and left her in the care of the princess's old nanny, until such time as the princess grew up and could look after her herself.''

''The way I live with Nanny?'' Cassie tipped her head and looked at Suzanne curiously.

''Exactly like that, Cassandra. Because, you see, you are that little girl. And Imogen is the princess.''

Imogen shrank before the serious look Cassie turned her way. ''How do you know she is, Grandmother?''

''Because,'' Suzanne said, her eyes suspiciously bright, ''I am the wicked queen who took you away from her. It was a very wrong thing to do, and I am deeply sorry for what I did.'' She lifted her head and met the gazes directed her way. At Mrs. Donnelly, openly weeping. At Mr. Donnelly, sitting as if he'd been turned to stone. At Mona, who watched Cassie like a mother hen. At Imogen, and lastly at Joe, who clasped Imogen's hand in his and was hanging on to it as if it were a life raft. ''I hope,'' she said, ''that you can forgive me. All of you.''

Into the silence that followed, Cassie said, ''Who's the prince?''

Suzanne swallowed. ''Well,'' she said, and swallowed

again, "Joe is. Imogen is your mother, and Joe is your father."

"Oh." Cassie took that under consideration for a moment that, to Imogen, seemed to stretch halfway to eternity. "Are you going to take me away from them again? Is that why you came here, to tell me I can't live with them, after all?"

"No," Joe said, going over and squatting in front of her. "No one will ever keep you away from us again, Cassie. When you come to live here next week, you'll be coming home for good. And every Christmas and Thanksgiving and birthday, all the people who love you will be here, too, to help you celebrate."

"There's only Nanny to do that," she said bluntly, "although Grandmother is always very nice to me. But she doesn't really like me to mess up her clothes, you know, or get dirt on her."

"Well, from now on, all that's going to change." He lifted her from Suzanne's lap and set her on her feet. "There are a lot of people who love you, honey, starting with your mommy and me."

"There's me," Mrs. Donnelly said, holding out her arms. "I'm your other grandma, darling, and this is your grandpa."

Imogen held her breath. Joe stood as if he teetered on the edge of a steep cliff. Suzanne allowed a tear to trickle down her cheek and made no attempt to wipe it away. Cassie looked at the faces surrounding her. "Is that all?" she asked. "I think I'd like a sister, as well."

The laughter was probably out of proportion, but it worked a miracle. The tension evaporated, swept away in a huge wave of relief as Cassie allowed herself to be hugged and kissed.

"Some day soon you'll meet your aunt and uncle and cousins," Mrs. Donnelly promised.

"And we'll do our best to give you a sister," Joe said, putting his arm around Imogen and holding her close.

"I think," Suzanne said, her emotions firmly under control again, "that I would like to take us all out to celebrate with dinner at the Norbury. I hear they have a very fine dining room."

Cassie looked at her suspiciously. "Are you still a wicked queen?"

"No, dear. From now on, I'll just be your grandmother."

"That's good," Cassie said. "Because in my storybook, the wicked queen gave Snow White a poisoned apple, you know."

"There'll be no poisoned apples on the table tonight, dear, nor any other night, either. Your father's right, Cassandra. You've come home to your family, and we'll never again do anything to hurt you."

It was after eight when they got back to the farm. "Well, I don't fool myself that it's all going to be plain sailing from here on," Joe said, linking his fingers with Imogen's as they walked from the car to the house, "but I think the worst is over, princess."

"Yes." Imogen sighed and looked at the moon riding just above the butternut trees. "Your mother was so sweet to me, Joe. And your father, too. I wish my mother could be as affectionate with you."

"Hey, miracles happen," he said. "I came back to Rosemont and found the love of my life and a daughter I didn't know I had. Given that, anything's possible."

It was that time of day that only comes in late summer, when the air is tinted violet and the leaves hang on the trees like painted shadows. A hushed and peaceful time, made for lovers.

Next week at the same time, Cassie would be sleeping upstairs, with Mona just down the hall. In another two months it would be Thanksgiving, with two families gathered around the long dining room table. But the blessings had come early that year.

"We have so much to be grateful for," Imogen said, looking over the sleeping land.

Joe took her in his arms and bent his mouth to hers. "And so much still to do, princess. As I understand it, a baby has to cook for nine months before it's ready to come out of the oven. What say we get started?"

EPILOGUE

NOTED in the Rosemont-on-the-Lake *Daily Herald* on Tuesday, June 2:

Couple Renew Wedding Vows

Last Saturday, Mrs. Geoffrey Palmer of Deepdene Grange hosted a garden reception following a ceremony in which her daughter, Imogen, and son-in-law, Joseph Donnelly, both formerly of Rosemont, renewed their wedding vows with their nine-year-old daughter, Cassandra, acting as maid of honor. The bride wore an ankle-length gown of lavender poie de soie accented with French lace and carried a bouquet of stephanotis. Her attendant was dressed in white silk and carried a basket of daisies. Among the guests were the groom's parents, Mr. and Mrs. Patrick Donnelly, his sister, Patricia, brother, Sean, sister-in-law, Elizabeth, and nephews Dennis and Jack. Tanya Rydahl of Vancouver, B.C., a close friend of the bride, was also present.

And one month later, in the birth announcements in *The Norbury Times* on Monday, July 1:

Donnelly: Joe and Imogen, née Palmer, are pleased to announce the birth of their son, Patrick, 8 lbs. 6 ozs., born Friday, June 28, at Norbury Cottage Hospital. A brother for Cassie.

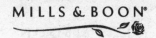

MILLS & BOON®

*M*akes
any time
special

Enjoy a romantic novel from
Mills & Boon®

Presents™ *Enchanted*™ *Temptation*.

Historical Romance™ *Medical Romance*™

4 FREE

books and a surprise gift!

We would like to take this opportunity to thank you for reading this Mills & Boon® book by offering you the chance to take FOUR more specially selected titles from the Presents™ series absolutely FREE! We're also making this offer to introduce you to the benefits of the Reader Service™—

- ★ FREE home delivery
- ★ FREE gifts and competitions
- ★ FREE monthly Newsletter
- ★ Books available before they're in the shops
- ★ Exclusive Reader Service discounts

Accepting these FREE books and gift places you under no obligation to buy, you may cancel at any time, even after receiving your free shipment. Simply complete your details below and return the entire page to the address below. *You don't even need a stamp!*

YES! Please send me 4 free Presents books and a surprise gift. I understand that unless you hear from me, I will receive 6 superb new titles every month for just £2.30 each, postage and packing free. I am under no obligation to purchase any books and may cancel my subscription at any time. The free books and gift will be mine to keep in any case.

P9EA

Ms/Mrs/Miss/Mr.................................Initials ....
                                                                          BLOCK CAPITALS PLEASE

Surname ....

Address ....

....

....Postcode...............................

Send this whole page to:
THE READER SERVICE, FREEPOST CN81, CROYDON, CR9 3WZ
(Eire readers please send coupon to: P.O. BOX 4546, DUBLIN 24.)

He's a cop, she's his prime suspect

MARY LYNN BAXTER

HARD CANDY

He's crossed the line no cop ever should.
He's involved with a suspect—his
prime suspect.

Falling for the wrong man is far down her
list of troubles.

Until he arrests her for murder.

MIRA®   **Available from 18th December 1998**